Commando

annual 1990

Printed and Published in Great Britain by D. C. THOMSON & CO., LTD.,
185 Fleet Street, London EC4A 2HS © D. C. THOMSON & CO., LTD., 1989.

ISBN 0-85116-448-X

Contents

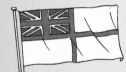

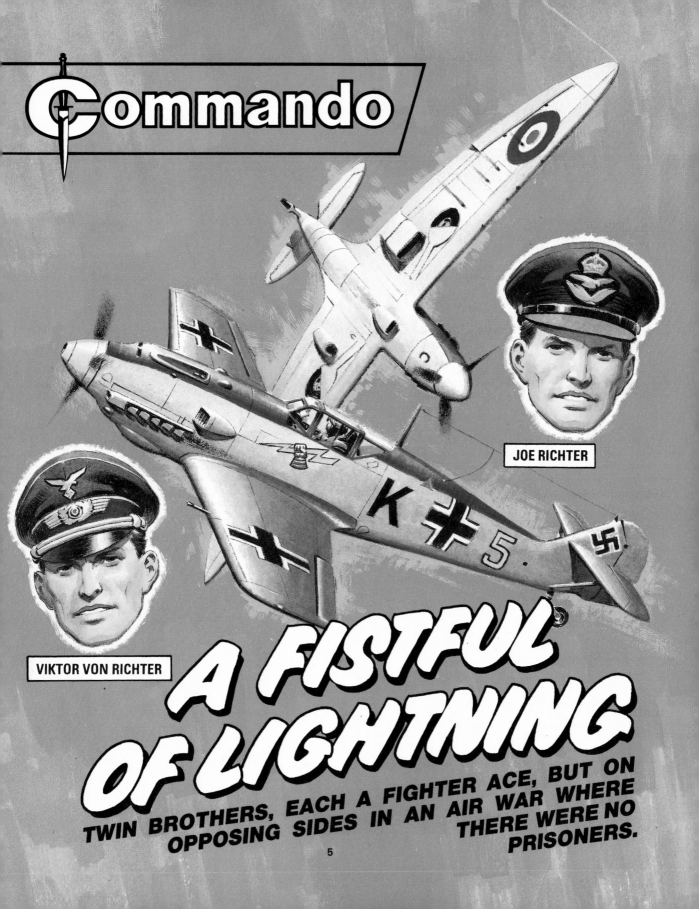

Commando

JOE RICHTER

VIKTOR VON RICHTER

A FISTFUL OF LIGHTNING

TWIN BROTHERS, EACH A FIGHTER ACE, BUT ON OPPOSING SIDES IN AN AIR WAR WHERE THERE WERE NO PRISONERS.

1918 — ABOVE THE TRENCHES OF THE WESTERN FRONT MAJOR GUNTHER VON RICHTER, A GERMAN ACE OF ACES, SCORED YET ANOTHER VICTORY IN HIS DISTINCTIVELY MARKED MACHINE.

ENGLANDER, YOU FOUGHT WELL. I SALUTE YOU.

HOWEVER, WARS END AND THE LATE 1920's FOUND GUNTHER VON RICHTER THE REPRESENTATIVE OF A GERMAN ENGINEERING COMPANY IN THE LAND OF FORMER ENEMIES, MARRIED TO AN ENGLISH GIRL AND WITH TWIN SONS — UNTIL OVERCOME WITH A SUDDEN LONGING FOR HIS HOMELAND . . .

YOUR MOTHER AND I HAVE DECIDED TO PART, MYSELF TO RETURN TO THE FATHERLAND WHILE SHE REMAINS IN ENGLAND. YOU ARE MY SONS AND I EXPECT YOU TO ACCOMPANY ME.

BUT YOU MAKE YOUR OWN CHOICE, DEARS. ON THAT WE ARE AGREED.

FATHER, I HONOUR MY MOTHER, BUT MY DUTY IS WITH YOU.

VIKTOR, I EXPECTED NO LESS OF YOU. BUT WHAT OF JOHANN?

FATHER, I CHOOSE TO STAY. I LOOK ON THIS COUNTRY AS MY HOME.

THIS I DID NOT EXPECT, JOHANN — YET I SHALL KEEP MY WORD.

SO THE VON RICHTER FAMILY BROKE UP . . .

FATHER WAS COLD IN HIS GOODBYE, MOTHER. HE THINKS I HAVE BETRAYED HIM IN NOT WISHING TO BE GERMAN.

HE IS HURT, JOE. IN TIME IT WILL HEAL.

NINE YEARS LATER, AT A PRIVATE AIRFIELD IN THE MIDLANDS IN THE SPRING OF 1939 . . .

A NICE JOB, JOE. I'D SAY YOU'VE EARNED YOUR HOUR IN THE MOTH.

GOSH THANKS! I NEED A MAP-READING FLIGHT FOR MY NAVIGATION TEST.

JOE'S JUST CRAZY ABOUT FLYING. I HEARD HE GOT HIS SCHOOL CERTIFICATE, BUT THREW AWAY A STEADY JOB IN A BANK JUST TO BE A DOGS-BODY NEAR PLANES WITH US.

QUITE TRUE. I PASSED HIM FOR HIS PRIVATE LICENCE THE DAY AFTER HE CAME OF AGE.

MY FIRST LEG IS ALONG THE RAILWAY LINE.

MEANWHILE, IN LONDON AT THE AIR MINISTRY . . .

ODD CASE, SIR. AN ENGLISH MOTHER AND ADOPTED BY HER BROTHER MAKES VON RICHTER LEGALLY BRITISH, BUT HIS BIRTH CERTIFICATE SHOWS HIS REAL FATHER TO BE GERMAN.

GUNTHER VON RICHTER? I'LL BE DASHED! CAN'T BE TWO JERRIES WITH THAT NAME.

WE COULD TURN DOWN THE LAD AS BEING A BIT SUSPECT, SIR.

NO DOUBT, BUT I REMEMBER VON RICHTER FROM THE WAR — A HARD ENEMY, BUT CLEAN AND STRAIGHT.

JOE RICHTER HAD LIVED WITH HIS UNCLE SINCE HIS MOTHER'S DEATH —

YOUR LETTER CAME BY SECOND POST, LAD — ON THE SIDEBOARD.

AT LAST! GOOD NEWS OR BAD?

UNCLE, I'M IN! THE RAF'S ACCEPTED ME FOR FLIGHT TRAINING ON THE BASIS OF A SHORT TERM COMMISSION.

THEN I WAS RIGHT TO INSIST YOU WENT FOR THE INTERVIEW IN A CLEAN SHIRT WITH CLEAN FINGERNAILS.

FATHER, I WONDER WHAT YOU'D MAKE OF ME JOINING THE RAF. WHERE ARE YOU AND VIKTOR? OH, IF ONLY YOU'D ANSWERED JUST ONE OF MY LETTERS!

SEPTEMBER, 1939, WORLD WAR II BROKE OUT AND THERE BEGAN SEVEN INACTIVE MONTHS OF THE "PHONEY WAR" THAT ENDED WITH THE GERMAN BREAKTHROUGH THAT LED TO THE BRITISH EVACUATION FROM DUNKIRK . . .

WHERE ARE OUR PLANES? WHERE'S THE RAF?

MEANWHILE AT A FIGHTER STATION IN THE SOUTH OF ENGLAND —

ANOTHER FLIGHT OF HURRICANES FROM SCOTLAND, SIR.

GET THEM REFUELLED AND AIRBORNE.

ONE OF THE NEW PILOTS WAS ACTING PILOT OFFICER JOE RICHTER —

GRAB COFFEE AND SANDWICHES WHILE YOUR AIRCRAFT ARE FUELLING, CHAPS. AFTER THAT, YOU'RE OFF TO DUNKIRK.

SHORTLY AFTER TAKE-OFF —

GRAB ALL THE HEIGHT WE CAN, CHAPS. WE'LL NEED IT OVER THE BEACHES.

MINUTES LATER, JOE SPOTTED HIS FIRST ENEMY.

BANDITS LOW AT THREE O'CLOCK! STUKAS!

8

9

JOE RELUCTANTLY TOOK TO THE SILK AND HAVING SURVIVED THE EXIT LOOKED FORWARD TO A WET LANDING . . .

SHOT DOWN ON MY FIRST SORTIE! TOO MUCH THINKING, TOO LITTLE DOING — AS FATHER WOULD HAVE SAID.

. . . BUT IN THE CROWDED WATERS OFF DUNKIRK JOE'S WAIT FOR RESCUE WAS SHORT.

AHOY!

DUNKIRK IS ONLY THE END OF ROUND ONE, CHAPS! THIS IS WHEN THE REAL WAR BEGINS.

WITH A TEMPORARY SURPLUS OF MORE PILOTS THAN FIGHTERS, JOE WAS GRANTED TWO DAYS' LEAVE.

HOME AGAIN, JOE? THERE'S A LETTER FOR YOU. CAME BY WAY OF SWITZERLAND AND HAS BEEN BLUE-STAMPED AS SEEN BY THE CENSOR'S OFFICE.

IT'S FROM FATHER — AND IT'S OVER A YEAR OLD.

SON JOHANN. SOON THERE WILL BE A WAR AND YOU WILL BECOME THE ENEMY OF MYSELF AND YOUR BROTHER. I EXPECT YOU TO DO YOUR DUTY TO THE MOTHERLAND YOU HAVE CHOSEN. YOU HAVE MY BLESSING.

BAD NEWS, JOE?

BAD — AND GOOD. I'D BETTER GET CHANGED IF I'M TO HELP DIG THE GARDEN!

LEAVE OVER, JOE REJOINED HIS SQUADRON "AT A FIGHTER STATION IN HAMPSHIRE" AND FLEW SORTIES TO PROTECT CHANNEL SHIPPING.

NO SIGN OF ANY ME109'S, SO — TALLY-HO!

THEN, AFTER ONE DESPERATE MANOEUVRE HE BROKE CLEAR, BUT—

THAT 109 — DOES IT REALLY HAVE A FISTFUL OF LIGHTNING EMBLEM ON IT?

THE CROWDED SKY WAS SUDDENLY EMPTY...

COULD IT BE FATHER? NO — NOT AT HIS AGE. WAS IT VIKTOR? OR DID I IMAGINE IT?

THE REAL WAR FINALLY BEGAN ON A DAY IN JULY...

KERRIPES — JERRY'S HERE! *SCRAMBLE!*

THE SQUADRON TRIED A DESPERATE TAKE-OFF UNDER BOMBING...

PHEW — MADE IT! BUT WHO MOVED THESE TREES SO CLOSE TO THE END OF THE RUNWAY?

JOE'S WAS ONE OF TWO HURRICANES THAT OVERTOOK THE DEPARTING HEINKELS...

TOP COVER OF TWO ME109's SWOOPED DOWN TO PROTECT THEIR FLOCK.

THEY'VE GOT GINGER!

A COLD ANGER SENT JOE ON A VENGEANCE HUNT.

ONE DOWN — NOW FOR HIS PARTNER.

THE NEXT FEW MOMENTS WERE HECTIC BUT —

I GOT BOTH OF 'EM! ONLY ONE OF 'EM MUST HAVE PUT A FEW ROUNDS INTO ME. OIL PRESSURE'S FALLING.

JOE DIDN'T QUITE MAKE IT BACK TO HIS AERODROME . . .

ARTHUR, I RECKON THAT MUST BE A REAL THIRSTY YOUNG FELLOW.

WELCOME TO THE GOAT AND COMPASSES, SIR.

MY WORD, THIS IS WHAT I CALL SERVICE.

JOE WAS COLLECTED AFTER A TELEPHONE CALL AND BACK AT HIS BASE —

CARE TO MEET ONE OF THOSE JERRIES YOU SHOT DOWN, JOE? THE RATION WAGON PICKED HIM UP ON THE ROAD.

AND IN THE OFFICERS' MESS —

VON RICHTER! VIKTOR!

DASHED IF FRITZ THINKS HE RECOGNISES YOU, JOE.

JOE SPOKE TO THE CAPTURED PILOT IN GERMAN . . .

I AM JOHANN VON RICHTER. I HAVE A BROTHER NAMED VIKTOR. IS HE IN THE LUFTWAFFE AND DOES HE HAVE A FISTED LIGHTNING BOLT PAINTED ON HIS AIRCRAFT?

HE IS — HE DOES. ACH, I SAY NO MORE. YOU ARE SO LIKE HIM, YET YOU ARE ENGLANDER — THE ENEMY.

I REALLY CANNOT ALLOW THIS FRATERNISING WITH THE ENEMY. HAVE THAT PRISONER LOCKED IN THE GUARDROOM TILL THE MILITARY POLICE COLLECT HIM.

JOE WAS SUMMONED BEFORE THE GROUP CAPTAIN . . .

RICHTER, I ASSUME YOUR CHATTER WITH THAT GERMAN WAS TO GLEAN INFORMATION USEFUL TO OUR INTELLIGENCE.

IT WAS NOT, SIR. I THINK IT WOULD BE A BIT CHEAP TO USE MY FAMILY BACKGROUND FOR SUCH A PURPOSE.

RICHTER HAS PROVED HIS LOYALTY, SIR. ONE OF MY BEST PILOTS.

OVER THE NEXT THREE MONTHS THE BATTLE OF BRITAIN RAGED, BEGINNING AS DAYTIME ONSLAUGHTS BY THE GERMAN LUFTWAFFE ON AIRFIELDS AND RADAR STATIONS IN SOUTHERN ENGLAND . . . AND AMONG THE FEW HUNDRED DEFENDING RAF PILOTS WAS JOE RICHTER.

FINISH FOR ONE STUKA. BUT WHAT IF IT HAD BEEN A 109 WITH THE EMBLEM OF A FISTFUL OF LIGHTNING? WOULD I HAVE BEEN ABLE TO FIRE?

EVEN SO, I'M NOT HAPPY ABOUT THIS GERMAN CONNECTION. MIGHT BE AN IDEA TO MAKE A SPECIAL NOTE ON HIS SERVICE SHEET.

BUT JOE WAS SPARED THAT GRIM DECISION FOR IN SEPTEMBER THE LUFTWAFFE CONCEDED DEFEAT AND SWITCHED TO NIGHT BOMBING. IN THE MONTHS THAT FOLLOWED, JOE'S SQUADRON CHANGED OVER TO SPITFIRES AND CARRIED THE WAR TO THE ENEMY IN SORTIES ACROSS OCCUPIED FRANCE. THEN —

HOME AGAIN, JOE?

EMBARKATION LEAVE, UNCLE. THE WHOLE SQUADRON'S MAKING A MOVE, BUT WE DON'T KNOW WHERE.

IN MARCH, 1942, JOE BOARDED AN AIRCRAFT CARRIER TO JOIN HIS CRATED SPITFIRE WHICH WAS RECONSTRUCTED ON THE PERILOUS VOYAGE TO THE BESIEGED MEDITERRANEAN ISLAND OF MALTA.

THEN, IN FLYING RANGE OF MALTA, CAME THE FIRST LAUNCH —

BARNEY'S MADE IT — JUST! SO A SPIT CAN TAKE OFF FROM A CARRIER.

REVVING HARD AGAINST LOCKED BRAKES, JOE REACHED FULL POWER BEFORE RELEASING THE BRAKES AND ROARING DOWN THE FLIGHT DECK — THEN INTO THE AIR.

TWENTY MINUTES LATER —

MAKE FOR THE SMOKE, GOSLING SQUADRON. LOOKS LIKE WE'RE IN TIME FOR A PARTY.

ACHTUNG! SPITFEUR!

MALTA WAS ANOTHER BATTLE OF BRITAIN WITH A HANDFUL OF RAF FIGHTERS TAKING ON OVERWHELMING ODDS. THE NEW ARRIVALS WERE FORCED TO LAND ON A BOMB CRATERED AIRSTRIP.

LOOK OUT!

JOE, THE SKIPPER NEEDS A COUPLE OF IDIOTS FOR A SPECIAL JOB. I VOLUNTEERED US.

BARNEY, YOU'RE THE SORT OF PAL I DON'T NEED.

YOUR TARGET IS THE FIGHTER FIELD NEAR RAGUSA IN SICILY. SLIPPER TANKS WILL GIVE YOU THE RANGE AND YOU'LL BOMB UP WITH A BRACE OF TWO-FIFTY POUNDERS.

JOE AND HIS PARTNER TOOK OFF IN DARKNESS —

AT 20,000 FEET THEY CROSSED THE MALTA CHANNEL . . .

HERE'S THE DAWN! DITCH TANKS AND COMMENCE DESCENT.

THE SPITFIRES CAME IN OUT OF THE RISING SUN . . .

WE'VE CAUGHT THEM NAPPING.

ONE MORE PASS, JOE! MAKE THE RUN-IN FROM THE NORTH.

BUT THE GROUND DEFENCES WERE NOW ALERT . . . AND ON TARGET.

BANDITS THREE O'CLOCK! TIME TO GO, BARNEY.

TOO LATE, JOE. CAUGHT SOME FLAK . . . MY LEGS.

I'LL COVER YOU, BARNEY. JUST KEEP GOING.

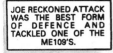

JOE RECKONED ATTACK WAS THE BEST FORM OF DEFENCE AND TACKLED ONE OF THE ME109'S.

ONE DOWN . . . WHERE'S THE OTHER?

I'M HIT! HOW DID HE GET THERE?

JOE MANAGED TO PULL OUT OF THE SPIN . . .

A FISTFUL OF LIGHTNING! I'M SURE OF IT!

THE SPITFIRE FLIPPED OVER AS JOE FOUGHT FOR CONTROL.

BACK STICK, HARD OPPOSITE RUDDER . . . AHH, CONTROLS FLOPPY. THAT JERRY DAMAGED ME BADLY.

THERE'S THAT JERRY FIELD! WELL, I'M NOT GOING MUCH FURTHER WITH THIS OLD BUS FLYING LIKE A BRICK.

DOWN IN ONE PIECE — BUT IF I GET OUT ALIVE I MUSTN'T LET JERRY GET MY KITE.

17

USING HIS FLARE PISTOL JOE SET HIS PANCAKED MACHINE ON FIRE BEFORE BEING PICKED UP . . .

AT LEAST NOBODY HAS SAID TO ME, "FOR YOU THE WAR IS OVER!"

THAT PLANE . . . A FISTFUL OF LIGHTNING! I'M REALLY SEEING IT.

JOHANN! SO WE MEET AT LAST!

VIKTOR! SO IT IS YOU PILOTING THE FISTFUL OF LIGHTNING.

GENTLEMEN, ALLOW ME TO INTRODUCE MY ENGLISH BROTHER.

WUNDERBAR — FAMILY REUNION! THIS CALLS FOR A PARTY.

WITH A LOT OF FAMILY GOSSIP TO CATCH UP ON JOE AND HIS BROTHER TALKED . . .

OH, YES, OUR DEAR FATHER IS IN ACTION. TOO OLD FOR FIGHTERS, BUT HE WANGLED COMMAND OF A SQUADRON OF JU-52 TRANSPORTS ON THE EASTERN FRONT.

A FINE PARTY, BUT THE TIME HAS COME TO THINK OF DUTY. I SHALL PERSONALLY ESCORT MY BROTHERLY ENEMY TO THE GUARDROOM.

NICE BLOKES!

A GOOD CROWD — BUT FOLLOW ME! A SHORT CUT.

ROUND THE CORNER —

FIRST, JOHANN, MY HAUPTMANN'S TUNIC FOR DISGUISE. OUT ON THE FIELD IS THE BIPLANE USED BY OUR AIRFIELD COMMANDER. NOW, STRIKE ME ON THE JAW AND GO.

YOU'RE LETTING ME GO? NO, VIKTOR! I WON'T GET YOU INTO TROUBLE.

JOHANN, YOU THINK OF YOURSELF AS ENGLISH BUT THE GESTAPO WILL REGARD YOU AS A GERMAN WHO IS FIGHTING FOR THE ENEMY. YOU COULD BE SHOT AS A TRAITOR, SO THINK OF OUR FATHER'S SHAME — AND HIT ME.

WELL, IF YOU INSIST . . .

SORRY, VIKTOR.

WIEDERSEHEN, JOHANN, MY BROTHER.

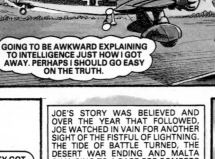

JOE ARRIVED BACK ON MALTA IN A HENSCHEL BIPLANE — AN HS123 . . .

GOING TO BE AWKWARD EXPLAINING TO INTELLIGENCE JUST HOW I GOT AWAY. PERHAPS I SHOULD GO EASY ON THE TRUTH.

CRIKEY! THAT'S A JERRY KITE!

JOE'S STORY WAS BELIEVED AND OVER THE YEAR THAT FOLLOWED, JOE WATCHED IN VAIN FOR ANOTHER SIGHT OF THE FISTFUL OF LIGHTNING. THE TIDE OF BATTLE TURNED, THE DESERT WAR ENDING AND MALTA CHANGING TO A BASE FOR BOMBERS CARRYING THE WAR TO THE ITALIAN MAINLAND. WHEN THE ALLIES LANDED IN SICILY, JOE'S SQUADRON WAS IN THE VANGUARD OF THE INVASION.

GAMEKEEPER TO WILD DUCKS, THE FIELD HAS BEEN CLEARED. YOU HAVE VACANT POSSESSION.

THE PAINTING ON THE WALL IDENTIFIED JOE'S NEW AIRFIELD AS VIKTOR'S OLD HOME.

THE JERRY OFFICERS' MESS, EH? WONDER WHAT THEY WERE LIKE.

MUCH LIKE US. I'D SAY THEY KNEW HOW TO THROW A GOOD PARTY.

AT THE DEBRIEFING —

BARNEY GOT BACK WITH A FEW SPLINTERS IN HIS LEGS. NOW, JOE, TELL ME AGAIN ABOUT YOUR ESCAPE.

I GOT SHOT DOWN AND WAS LUCKY ENOUGH TO BE ABLE TO GRAB THAT KITE AND FLY BACK.

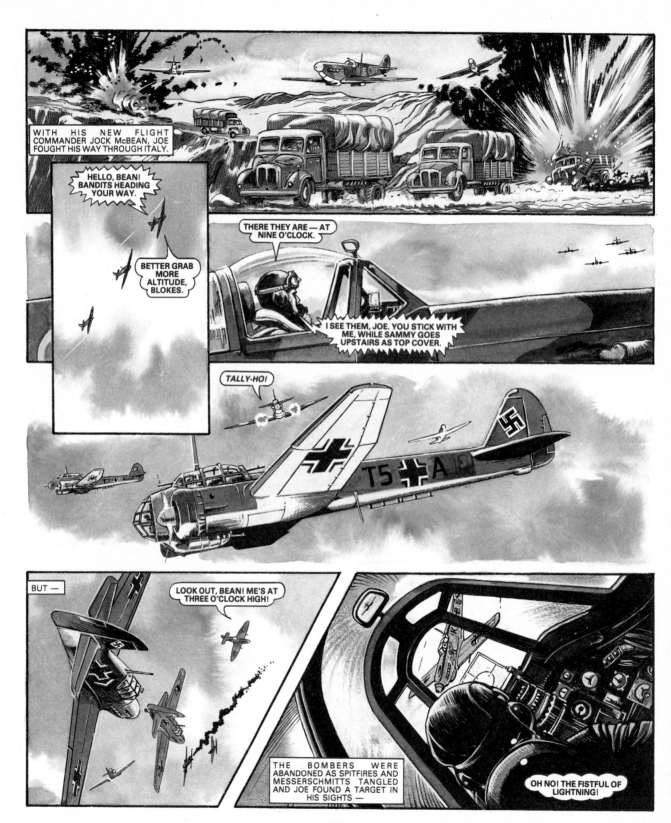

WITH HIS NEW FLIGHT COMMANDER JOCK McBEAN, JOE FOUGHT HIS WAY THROUGH ITALY.

HELLO, BEAN! BANDITS HEADING YOUR WAY.

BETTER GRAB MORE ALTITUDE, BLOKES.

THERE THEY ARE — AT NINE O'CLOCK.

I SEE THEM, JOE. YOU STICK WITH ME, WHILE SAMMY GOES UPSTAIRS AS TOP COVER.

TALLY-HO!

BUT —

LOOK OUT, BEAN! ME'S AT THREE O'CLOCK HIGH!

THE BOMBERS WERE ABANDONED AS SPITFIRES AND MESSERSCHMITTS TANGLED AND JOE FOUND A TARGET IN HIS SIGHTS —

OH NO! THE FISTFUL OF LIGHTNING!

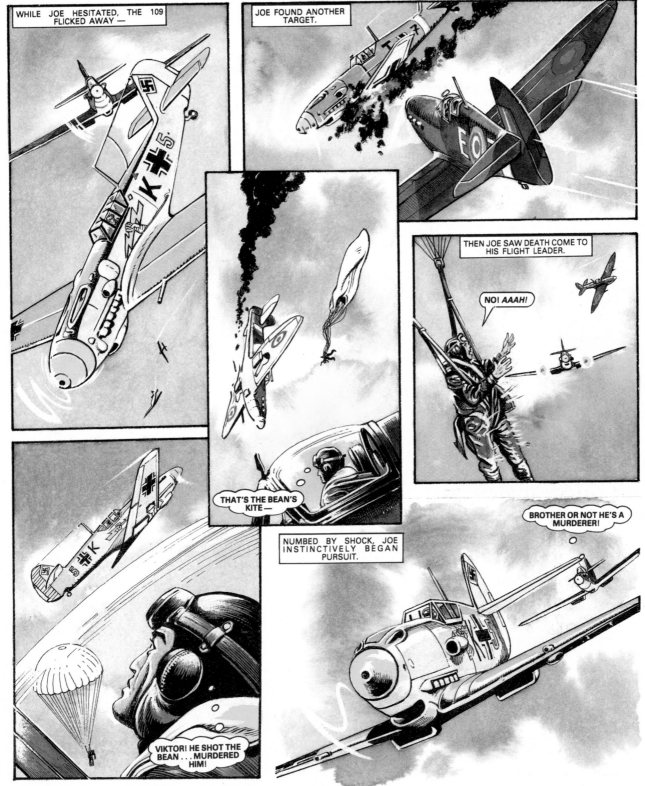

WHILE JOE HESITATED, THE 109 FLICKED AWAY —

JOE FOUND ANOTHER TARGET.

THAT'S THE BEAN'S KITE —

THEN JOE SAW DEATH COME TO HIS FLIGHT LEADER.

NO! *AAAH!*

NUMBED BY SHOCK, JOE INSTINCTIVELY BEGAN PURSUIT.

VIKTOR! HE SHOT THE BEAN . . . MURDERED HIM!

BROTHER OR NOT HE'S A MURDERER!

HE'S SEEN ME! HE'LL MOST LIKELY TURN THAT HALF-ROLL INTO A DIVE.

JOE CLOSED IN THEN PRESSED THE BUTTON . . .

THE MESSERSCHMITT MADE A HARD PANCAKE LANDING.

HE'S GOT OUT. WELL, HE'S NOT GETTING AWAY. I'VE LANDED ON WORSE STRIPS THAN DOWN THERE.

HE'S HIT HARD BUT HE'S UNDER CONTROL.

JOE LANDED HEAVILY BUT SAFELY.

HILFE! HELP ME!

THAT'S NOT VIKTOR'S VOICE!

WHAT HAS BECOME OF VON RICHTER?

THE ONE WHO FLEW THIS MACHINE BEFORE I JOINED THE SQUADRON? HE WENT BACK HOME UNDER ARREST. SOMETHING ABOUT ALLOWING A PRISONER TO ESCAPE.

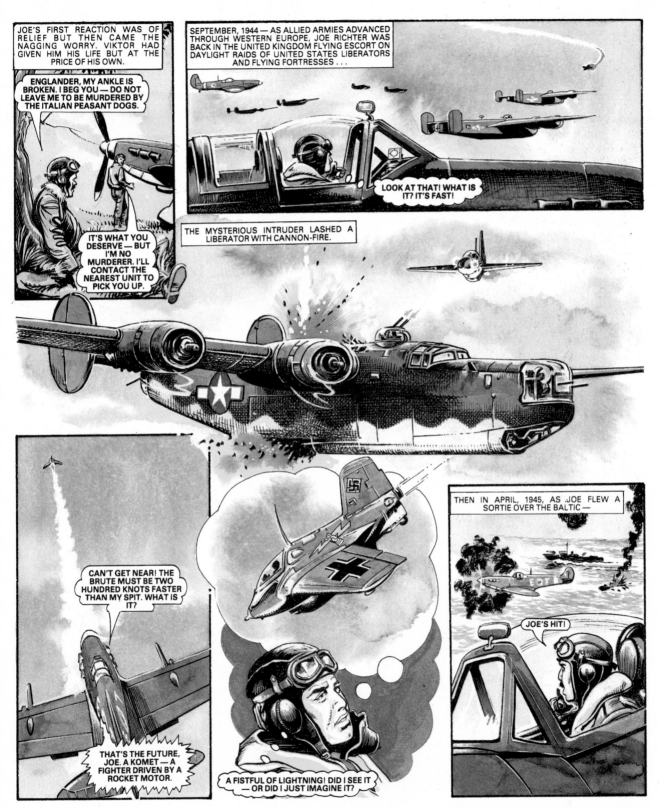

JOE'S FIRST REACTION WAS OF RELIEF BUT THEN CAME THE NAGGING WORRY. VIKTOR HAD GIVEN HIM HIS LIFE BUT AT THE PRICE OF HIS OWN.

ENGLANDER, MY ANKLE IS BROKEN. I BEG YOU — DO NOT LEAVE ME TO BE MURDERED BY THE ITALIAN PEASANT DOGS.

IT'S WHAT YOU DESERVE — BUT I'M NO MURDERER. I'LL CONTACT THE NEAREST UNIT TO PICK YOU UP.

SEPTEMBER, 1944 — AS ALLIED ARMIES ADVANCED THROUGH WESTERN EUROPE, JOE RICHTER WAS BACK IN THE UNITED KINGDOM FLYING ESCORT ON DAYLIGHT RAIDS OF UNITED STATES LIBERATORS AND FLYING FORTRESSES . . .

LOOK AT THAT! WHAT IS IT? IT'S FAST!

THE MYSTERIOUS INTRUDER LASHED A LIBERATOR WITH CANNON-FIRE.

CAN'T GET NEAR! THE BRUTE MUST BE TWO HUNDRED KNOTS FASTER THAN MY SPIT. WHAT IS IT?

THAT'S THE FUTURE, JOE. A KOMET — A FIGHTER DRIVEN BY A ROCKET MOTOR.

A FISTFUL OF LIGHTNING! DID I SEE IT — OR DID I JUST IMAGINE IT?

THEN IN APRIL, 1945, AS JOE FLEW A SORTIE OVER THE BALTIC —

JOE'S HIT!

23

JOE HEADED FOR THE SHORE AND GAINED SOME ALTITUDE BEFORE ROLLING THE STRICKEN SPITFIRE AND BALING OUT...

...STRAIGHT INTO A RECEPTION COMMITTEE.

DO WE SHOOT HIM?

THAT WOULD BE UNKIND AFTER WHAT THE POOR LAD'S BEEN THROUGH. I'LL BE HAPPY JUST LOOTING HIS WRISTWATCH. YOU CAN HAVE HIS BOOTS.

JOE'S TRANSPORT WAS RAMSHACKLE BUT WELCOME.

IT'S THE AIRFIELD WE PASTED LAST WEEK.

TAKE HIM TO THE COLONEL OVER THERE BY THE ANNIE — THE JU-52.

THE FISTFUL OF LIGHTNING! THIS TIME I'M NOT IMAGINING IT.

FATHER!

VIKTOR? ACH, NO! YOU ARE JOHANN!

HERR LEUTNANT, I SURRENDER TO YOU THIS AIRCRAFT AND MY OWN PERSON.

SURRENDER? FATHER, WE ARE FIFTY MILES BEHIND YOUR LINES.

THAT SMOKE IS FROM OUR DEMOLITIONS, MY SON. IN A DAY OR TWO IVAN WILL BE HERE AND I WOULD PREFER THE WOUNDED ON THIS IRON ANNIE TO BE IN ALLIED HANDS. YOUR BROTHER IS AMONG THEM.

WHAT — VIKTOR? BUT I THOUGHT THE GESTAPO TOOK HIM!

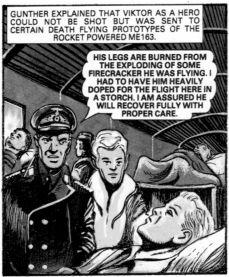

GUNTHER EXPLAINED THAT VIKTOR AS A HERO COULD NOT BE SHOT BUT WAS SENT TO CERTAIN DEATH FLYING PROTOTYPES OF THE ROCKET POWERED ME163.

HIS LEGS ARE BURNED FROM THE EXPLODING OF SOME FIRECRACKER HE WAS FLYING. I HAD TO HAVE HIM HEAVILY DOPED FOR THE FLIGHT HERE IN A STORCH. I AM ASSURED HE WILL RECOVER FULLY WITH PROPER CARE.

JOE ACCEPTED THE SURRENDER AND GUNTHER SUGGESTED THEY FLY TO THE ALLIED LINES.

I'M NOT QUALIFIED ON DUAL-ENGINES, FATHER. YOU'LL HAVE TO BE PILOT.

NATURALLY, SON JOHANN. I MAY BE YOUR PRISONER, BUT THAT DOES NOT MEAN ALLOWING YOU TO FLY MY OLD IRON ANNIE.

LATER —

A JU-52 DOING A WING WAGGLE AND FLYING A WHITE FLAG. LOOKS LIKE A SURRENDER.

WE'LL TAKE NO CHANCES. YOU LEAD THEM IN AND I'LL COVER YOU.

SOON ALL WILL BE WELL. VIKTOR WILL GET PROPER MEDICAL TREATMENT AND ALL OF US WILL BE FREE OF THE THREAT OF THE GESTAPO.

FOREWARNED BY RADIO A GROUND RECEPTION PARTY GREETED JOE AND HIS PRISONERS.

TOO LATE, W.O. THESE MEN ARE ALREADY MY PRISONERS — NOT BAD FOR AN UNARMED MAN, EH?

THIS IS WHERE WE PART, JOHANN, YOU TO YOUR DUTY AND VIKTOR AND I INTO THE CAGE. LOOK AFTER YOURSELF MY SON.

PERHAPS ONE DAY WE'LL BE TOGETHER AGAIN AS A FAMILY — BUT NOT A FAMILY AT WAR.

THE END

Commando

SAPPED!

A captured German Mark IV tank after it is destroyed on the battlefield by a Royal Engineers' demolition charge.

Commando

A broken regimental cane bridges a thirty-year gap and brings together two families at war.

DEBT OF HONOUR

PRIVATE SAM TARRANT WAS HOME ON LEAVE CELEBRATING HIS TWENTIETH BIRTHDAY. IT WAS APRIL, 1944, AND AS THE PARTY WENT ON SAM WAS UNAWARE THAT HE WAS ABOUT TO BE CAUGHT UP IN EVENTS FROM ANOTHER WAR.

WE'RE GOING TO GIVE THE JERRIES WHAT FOR THIS TIME! I JUST CAN'T WAIT TO GET OVER THERE!

THAT'S THE SPIRIT, SAM. THE ONLY GOOD JERRY IS A DEAD JERRY, EH LAD?

THE LONG-AWAITED SECOND FRONT, THE INVASION OF EUROPE, WAS EXPECTED AT ANY TIME.

YOU'RE QUIET, UNCLE GEORGE. SORRY YOU CAN'T HAVE ANOTHER CRACK AT THE HUN, EH?

I'D LIKE A WORD, SAM — ALONE!

SAM'S UNCLE GEORGE HAD BEEN AN INFANTRY COMPANY SERGEANT MAJOR IN THE FIRST WORLD WAR AND HAD BEEN WOUNDED ON THE SOMME.

I RECKON YOU HAVE MORE REASON THAN MOST TO HATE THE JERRIES, UNCLE GEORGE. THEY PUT YOU IN THIS WHEELCHAIR.

THEY'RE NOT ALL BAD, SAM. MOST OF 'EM ARE JUST DOING THEIR DUTY — LIKE YOU. I WOULDN'T BE ALIVE IF IT HADN'T BEEN FOR ONE PARTICULAR JERRY.

AT GEORGE'S REQUEST THEY STOPPED AND THE OLD MAN PRODUCED A TREASURED MEMENTO FROM THE BOX ON HIS KNEES.

THAT'S YOUR OLD C.S.M.'s CANE, ISN'T IT, UNCLE GEORGE? WHAT HAPPENED TO THE OTHER HALF?

IT WAS TRADITION, SAM, THAT OUR C.S.M. ALWAYS CARRIED THE COMPANY BATON, EVEN INTO ACTION.

B COMPANY YORK AND

28

THE BEACH-HEAD ESTABLISHED, BRITISH AND CANADIAN FORCES MOVED ON CAEN. FIGHTING WAS FIERCE.

WINDOW, SAM! AAAARGH!

JOHNNY'S BOUGHT IT!

SAM'S VENGEANCE WAS QUICK — AND FINAL.

AAAARGH!

THAT'S FOR JOHNNY!

AS THE ALLIES SWEPT ON THROUGH FRANCE INTO GERMANY AND ACROSS THE RHINE, SAM SUFFERED NOT A SCRATCH, YET HE RARELY GAVE A THOUGHT TO THE GOOD LUCK TOKEN HE CARRIED.

THEN, DURING THE ASSAULT ON GREIBHAVEN —

AAAARGH!

LOOK OUT, SAM!

MEDICS!

HE ONLY NICKED ME, CHARLIE.

WHAT'VE YOU GOT THERE, MATE?

SUPPOSED TO BE MY GOOD LUCK TOKEN. IT WORKED — UNTIL NOW.

SAM SAW THE PRISONER REACH INSIDE HIS TUNIC AND SUSPECTED THE WORST.

YOUR LUCK'S STILL IN. YOU'VE A SURFACE WOUND. NOTHING SERIOUS!

CHARLIE, LOOK OUT!

AAAAH!

WHERE DID YOU GET THIS? WHO ARE YOU?

AS THE PRISONER FELL HE DREW FROM HIS TUNIC — NOT A GUN OR A GRENADE — BUT THE OTHER HALF OF UNCLE GEORGE'S CANE.

OH, NO! WHAT HAVE I DONE?

B COMPANY 6 BATTALION YORK AND LANCS

HE'S DEAD, FELLER.

SAM SEARCHED DESPERATELY THROUGH THE PRISONER'S POCKETS.

COME ON, SAM! GET UNDER COVER!

HERE ARE HIS PAPERS!

HANS MULLER COULD HAVE BEEN THE SON OF THE MAN WHO SAVED UNCLE GEORGE'S LIFE, CHARLIE — AND I KILLED HIM IN COLD BLOOD!

HANS MULLER

YOU WEREN'T TO KNOW WHAT HE WAS REACHING FOR, SAM! HE COULD HAVE HAD A GRENADE! YOU CAN'T BLAME YOURSELF FOR WHAT HAPPENED.

HAUNTED BY WHAT HE HAD DONE, SAM FOUGHT ON UNTIL APRIL, 1945, AND THE LAST DAYS OF THE ALLIED ADVANCE.

ALMHEIN   BREMFURT

CHARLIE, LOOK — ALMHEIN! THAT'S WHERE HANS MULLER'S FOLKS LIVE! THEIR ADDRESS IS ON HIS LETTER!

FORGET IT, SAM! WE'RE GOING ON TO BREMFURT.

BUT DESPITE CHARLIE'S PLEAS, SAM HEADED FOR ALMHEIM.

THIS IS DESERTION, SAM, YOU IDIOT! I'M COMING WITH YOU!

THAT LOOKS LIKE IT OVER THERE, CHARLIE! LOOK OUT FOR THE NAMEPLATE FOR RUEDESTRASSE.

THE PLACE LOOKS DESERTED, SAM. WE'RE IN NO-MAN'S LAND!

RUEDESTRASSE

RUEDESTRASSE! THIS IS IT, CHARLIE. LOOK FOR NUMBER 18.

HERE IT IS, CHARLIE! THIS IS WHERE HANS MULLER LIVED!

THIS IS MADNESS, SAM! WHAT ARE YOU GOING TO SAY TO THE OLD MAN? YOU SAVED MY UNCLE — SO I KILLED YOUR SON!

IN THE CELLAR, SAM FOUND A COWED CROWD OF CIVILIANS.

MULLER — HANS MULLER. I AM LOOKING FOR HIS FATHER.

I AM KARL MULLER. YOU BRING NEWS OF MY SON?

IT'S HIM, CHARLIE!

SAM'S THROAT WENT DRY AS HE APPROACHED THE AGING GERMAN. HE HELD OUT THE BROKEN CANE.

YOU — YOU KNOW ABOUT THIS?

YOU ARE THE MAN WHO SAVED MY UNCLE'S LIFE ON THE SOMME . . ?

MY — MY SON! HE IS DEAD?

AS THE OLD MAN'S HANDS CLOSED OVER SAM'S HE REMEMBERED WHAT UNCLE GEORGE HAD TOLD HIM. "THEY'RE NOT ALL BAD. THEY'RE DOING THEIR DUTY, JUST LIKE YOU." THEY, TOO, COULD GRIEVE . . .

YES. I'M SORRY.

SAM — GET DOWN!

ALERTED BY CHARLIE'S SHOUT, AS THE SHELLS BURST CLOSE, SAM FLUNG HIMSELF AT THE OLD MAN . . .

. . . AND TOOK THE FULL FORCE OF THE BLAST.

HE SAVED MY LIFE!

SAM! SAM!

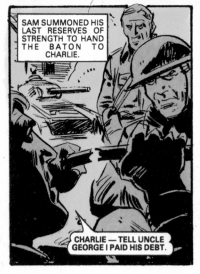

SAM SUMMONED HIS LAST RESERVES OF STRENGTH TO HAND THE BATON TO CHARLIE.

CHARLIE — TELL UNCLE GEORGE I PAID HIS DEBT.

I'LL TELL HIM, SAM! IT WAS A DEBT OF HONOUR — AND YOU'VE PAID IT IN FULL!

THE END

Commando

THE COWARD

Jonas Kyle knew just the label for the man who abandoned him at Dunkirk — COWARD! Yet the man he accused had been his best friend.

TOD GRAHAM AND TWINS JONAS AND JACK KYLE HAD BEEN MATES SINCE CHILDHOOD. FRIENDLY QUARRELS WERE NOISY AND FREQUENT AND USUALLY SOON FORGOTTEN. THEN CAME THE ACCIDENT — AND FRIENDSHIP WAS FORGOTTEN TO BE REPLACED BY A HATRED THAT COULD PROVE FATAL.

TEMPER, TEMPER, JONAS! YOU KNOW WHAT MA SAID. YOU'VE GOT TO TRY TO SEE THE FUNNY SIDE OF LIFE.

YOU ROTTEN SNAKE, JACK! I'M GOING TO TEAR YOUR HEAD OFF YOUR SHOULDERS!

LOOK, PACK IT IN! WE'RE SUPPOSED TO BE TRYING OUT THAT NEW SAIL!

ON THAT JULY DAY IN 1938 TOD GRAHAM HAD NO INKLING THAT THIS LATEST DIFFERENCE OF OPINION BETWEEN THE TWINS WAS TO SET OFF A CHAIN OF EVENTS THAT WAS TO HAVE SUCH A SHATTERING EFFECT ON HIS LIFE.

ONE OF THESE DAYS THAT TEMPER OF JONAS' IS GOING TO CAUSE YOU A REAL BUST-UP. BREAK IT UP, THE PAIR OF YOU!

IT'S JACK'S FAULT MOST OF THE TIME, GEORGE. HE LOVES TO GET JONAS GOING.

THIS VIPER, THIS TOAD, HAD ME WAITING AN HOUR OUTSIDE THE CHURCH HALL FOR MY DATE, WHILE ALL THE TIME HE WAS CHATTING HER UP.

CAN I HELP IT IF SHE FOUND ME BETTER LOOKING?

34

GEORGE NAYLOR HAD TRAINED THE LADS AS YACHTSMEN AND HAD EVEN AGREED TO TRY A NEW SAIL TO THEIR DESIGN.

COME ON, JONAS — WE'LL MISS THE TIDE!

WHO NEEDS HIM, TOD? COME ON.

I AIN'T GOING LIKE THIS! YOU WAIT FOR ME!

I WOULDN'T GO OUT PAST THE POINT, LADS. IT'S BLOWING UP A BIT OUT THERE. AND GET THOSE LIFEJACKETS ON!

AYE, AYE, SKIPPER!

WHEN JONAS GETS BACK, TELL HIM WE COULDN'T WAIT.

THE WIND WAS FRESH, BUT VISIBILITY WAS GOOD AND THERE WAS NO SIGN OF THE IMPENDING STORM.

STAND BY, TOD!

SEFTON POINT, THAT LONG FINGER OF GRANITE, PROTECTED GAULSEA BAY FROM THE RIGOURS OF THE ATLANTIC.

I'M STILL NOT HAPPY WITH THAT MAINSAIL, JACK.

DO YOU RECKON THERE'LL BE A WAR, TOD? MA SAYS THIS HITLER BLOKE'S GOT HIS MIND SET ON IT.

NO, HE WOULDN'T DARE . . . STRAIGHTEN HER UP, JACK!

THEN A SQUALL APPEARED OUT OF A CLEAR SKY.

TOD — LOOK!

COULD BE A BAD ONE! BRING HER ROUND. WE'LL TAKE HER HOME.

IT WAS LIKE NOTHING TOD HAD EXPERIENCED BEFORE. AS THE RAIN LASHED DOWN THE SEA WAS WHIPPED INTO A FRENZY.

STRIKE THE CANVAS, TOD! WE'LL GO OVER!

SHE'S STUCK!

TOD KNEW HE HAD TO FREE THE MAINSAIL.

KEEP HER BOW STEADY, JACK! IF WE GET HER BROADSIDE ON TO THIS SEA WE'VE HAD IT!

CAN'T HEAR YOU! WE'VE GOT TO GET BACK, TOD! WE'VE GOT TO GET BACK!

THEN JACK PANICKED AND SWUNG THE TILLER HARD OVER.

SHE CAN'T TAKE IT! GOT TO GET BACK . . !

NO! HOLD HER STEADY, JACK . . . AAAARGH!

HELP ME, JACK! DON'T LEAVE ME!

TOD COULD SEE THE SHEER TERROR ON HIS FRIEND'S FACE AS THE YACHT SPED AWAY.

THEN AS TOD WATCHED HELPLESSLY A GIANT WAVE STRUCK THE WANDERLUST AND SHE WAS SWAMPED.

JACK!

TOD SWAM TO THE UPTURNED BOAT AND SEARCHED THE FOAMING WATERS FOR HIS FRIEND.

JACK! JACK! WHERE ARE YOU?

JACK! YOU'VE GOT TO FIND JACK!

GEORGE NAYLOR HAD REPORTED THE LADS' PLIGHT AND TOD WAS PICKED UP WITHIN MINUTES. HIS ONE THOUGHT WAS FOR HIS FRIEND.

JONAS WAS WAITING AT THE QUAY.

WHERE'S JACK! TOD, WHAT HAPPENED! WHY DIDN'T YOU WAIT FOR ME?

THE GAULSEA LIFEBOAT FOUND JACK SOON AFTERWARDS. THAT STILL SHAPE HUDDLED UNDER A BLANKET ON THE BOW WAS TO HAUNT TOD IN THE YEARS TO COME.

JACK..? JACK! NO! NO!

JACK! WHY DIDN'T YOU WAIT FOR ME? JACK!

EASY NOW, SON — EASY!

JONAS' CRY LEFT TOD NUMB.

WHY? WHY? WHY?

SLEEPING AND WAKING, LIFE FOR TOD BECAME A NIGHTMARE.

I DON'T KNOW! LEAVE ME ALONE!

IF ONLY JACK HAD KEPT HIS HEAD, THE ACCIDENT WOULD NEVER HAVE HAPPENED. IT HAD BEEN SHEER PANIC THAT MOTIVATED JACK . . .

JACK HADN'T DELIBERATELY SAILED OFF AND LEFT TOD IN THE WATER. NO ONE MUST EVER BELIEVE THAT!

THEN CAME THE INQUEST.

JUST TAKE YOUR TIME, GRAHAM, AND TELL US IN YOUR OWN WORDS WHAT HAPPENED.

EVERYTHING WAS FINE. THEN — THEN THIS STORM CAME UP OUT OF NOWHERE . . .

IT WAS AN ADDED NIGHTMARE FOR TOD. HE COULDN'T TELL THEM THE TRUTH! HE WOULDN'T LAY THE BLAME ON JACK, BRAND HIS FRIEND INCOMPETENT — A COWARD!

I THINK I HAD THE TILLER . . . I DON'T REMEMBER!

YOU SHOULD HAVE WAITED FOR ME! WHY DIDN'T YOU WAIT?

SILENCE! GO ON, GRAHAM!

GEORGE NAYLOR TOLD HIS TALE THEN BERT LINDSAY, THE LIFEBOAT'S CREWMAN WHO'D PULLED JACK FROM THE WATER, TOLD HIS STORY.

HE WAS STILL ALIVE WHEN WE GOT HIM OUT OF THE WATER. HE KEPT SAYING, 'DON'T LEAVE ME! DON'T LEAVE ME!' HE DIED BEFORE WE REACHED THE HARBOUR.

37

REMOVE THAT YOUTH FROM THE COURT!

NO, JONAS! NO!

YOU LEFT JACK! YOU LEFT HIM TO DIE!

JONAS' OUTBURST HAD THE COURT IN UPROAR.

YOU KILLED HIM! YOU KILLED MY BROTHER! YOU COWARD!

THE VERDICT AT THE INQUEST WAS MISADVENTURE. THE VERDICT OF JONAS KYLE WAS MUCH MORE DAMNING.

IT SEEMED A THOUSAND EYES WERE WATCHING TOD — ACCUSING HIM.

I'LL GET EVEN WITH YOU, TOD GRAHAM! I'LL GET YOU IF IT'S THE LAST THING I EVER DO!

COME ON, JONAS! LEAVE IT, SON!

IN HIS HEART TOD KNEW THAT WITH HIS DYING BREATH JACK HAD BEEN ECHOING HIS OWN WORDS, NOT ACCUSING HIM . . .

HELP ME, JACK! DON'T LEAVE ME!

. . . BUT WHO WOULD BELIEVE HIM NOW?

TOD GAVE UP HIS JOB AS AN APPRENTICE BOAT-BUILDER AS LIFE FOR HIM IN GAULSEA BECAME INTOLERABLE.

THAT'S RIGHT! RUN AWAY, COWARD!

HIS PARENTS TRIED HARD TO EASE THE PAIN.

THE FIRM'S MOVING ME TO THE SOUTH COAST, TOD, WHITEHAVEN. IT'LL BE BETTER FOR YOU THERE.

WILL IT, DAD?

A NEW TOWN, NEW JOB, NEW LIFE? IT WASN'T THAT EASY FOR TOD.

YEAH, THAT'S HIM, I TELL YOU. LEFT HIS MATE TO DROWN, THEY SAY.

BUT SLOWLY TOD MANAGED TO ADAPT AND TO LIVE WITH HIS PAIN. HE BECAME A LONER, RETIRING WITHIN HIMSELF.

PEOPLE BEGAN TO FORGET . . .

I'LL LEAVE YOUR SHOPPING AT THE DOOR FOR YOU, MRS CARTER.

TOD'S SUCH A NICE, QUIET BOY, MRS GRAHAM. BUT I WAS ONLY SAYING TO MY DAUGHTER — YOU NEVER SEE HIM SMILE.

NO, DEAR, I THINK HE'S FORGOTTEN HOW.

1939 — AND THE NATION PREPARED FOR WAR.

ALL UNNECESSARY, LAD. THERE'LL BE NO WAR.

MA SAYS THIS HITLER BLOKE'S GOT HIS MIND SET ON IT.

NO, HE WOULDN'T DARE . . . STRAIGHTEN HER UP, JACK!

MAY, 1940. THE NEWS GOT WORSE EACH DAY.

FROM JONAS — OH, NO!

. . . AND AS GERMAN ARMOUR SWEEPS SOUTH BRITISH FORCES ARE REPORTED WITHDRAWING ON DUNKIRK. FIGHTING IS REPORTED TO BE HEAVY . . .

In deepest sympathy
Just so you don't forget!!!
Jack would have been
nineteen today
J.H.

TOD HAD HOPED JONAS' OUTBURST AT THE INQUEST HAD BEEN MADE IN THE HEAT OF THE MOMENT, THAT TIME WOULD HAVE HEALED THE SPLIT . . .

THINGS SOUND REAL BAD, TOD. WHO'S THE LETTER FROM?

JUST AN OLD FRIEND, MUM.

REPORTING FOR WORK NEXT MORNING TOD WAS TO FORGET ABOUT JONAS — FOR THE TIME BEING.

LOOK LIVELY, LADS! ADMIRALTY WANT EVERYTHING CAPABLE OF CROSSING THE CHANNEL TO RENDEZVOUS WITH CREWS IN THE SOUND BY NOON.

I'LL TAKE THE KETCH, BOSS. THE LUCKY STAR'S ALL TANKED UP, TOO!

COUNT ME IN, BOSS!

ME, TOO, MR MAITLAND!

NOON, AT THE SOUND — SMALL BOATS — HUNDREDS OF THEM. THEIR CREWS BAFFLED YET EAGER.

YOUR DESTINATION IS DUNKIRK! KEEP ASTERN OF ME! SHOULD YOU LOSE STATION, RETURN TO PORT! I REPEAT, RETURN TO PORT!

THEY MUST BE TAKING THE LADS OFF, TOD.

SOUNDS LIKE IT, MR MAITLAND. THIS COULD BE HOT!

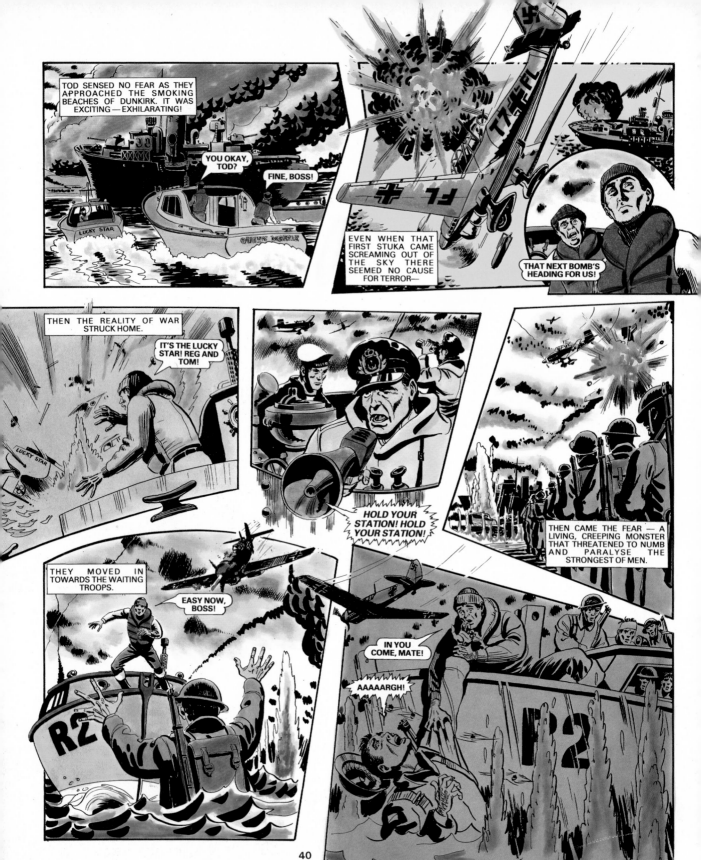

THE TROOPS WERE FERRIED OUT TO THE WAITING SHIPS.

UP YOU GO, LADS! LOOK LIVELY!

FEAR WAS FORGOTTEN NOW IN DETERMINATION TO COMPLETE THE JOB AT HAND.

WATCH IT, MATE! TAKE YOUR TURN!

GOLDEN ROSE

R2

TOD THOUGHT HIS IMAGINATION WAS PLAYING TRICKS. HE FELT HE RECOGNISED THAT VOICE . . .

ANY MORE FOR THE SKYLARK? MOVE ALONG DOWN THE BUS . . .! YOU!

JONAS!

OF ALL THE TIMES, OF ALL THE PLACES TO MEET UP WITH JONAS KYLE!

THAT'LL DO, FELLERS! WE'LL BE BACK!

A LOOK OF SHEER HATRED MADE IT CLEAR TO TOD THAT JONAS HAD NEITHER FORGOTTEN NOR FORGIVEN.

HERE THEY COME AGAIN!

AAARGH!

DAN!

TOD TOOK THE WHEEL.

I'M OKAY, TOD! GET BACK TO THE MEN!

TOD KNEW HIS BOSS WAS FAR FROM ALL RIGHT. HE FELT ALONE AND VULNERABLE.

THAT'S ENOUGH, FELLER! YOU'LL HAVE US OVER!

THE STUKAS RETURNED, SCREAMING DOWN TO UNLEASH THEIR DEADLY CARGOES.

THE BOAT AHEAD WAS HIT.

THAT'S THE GOLDEN ROSE — JONAS' BOAT!

MEN WERE STRUGGLING IN THE WATER, CRYING OUT FOR HELP. ONE VOICE SEEMED TO CARRY ABOVE THE REST — BITTER AND ACCUSING.

HELP US, TOD! HELP US, MAN!

I CAN'T! I'M OVERLOADED!

DON'T LEAVE US! YOU COWARD! YOU LOUSY COWARD.

THEN THE WATER ERUPTED AS A CRESCENDO OF SOUND DROWNED OUT THE PITIFUL CRIES.

JONAS! OH, NO!

FROM THAT MOMENT ON TOD MOVED AUTOMATICALLY. HIS MIND SEEMED NUMB. IT WAS AS IF TIME HAD STOPPED WITH JONAS' LAST SICKENING CRY.

ALL THE WAY BACK TO ENGLAND AND AFTERWARDS IT WAS A CRY THAT WAS TO HAUNT HIM FOR MONTHS TO COME.

WELL DONE, LAD. YOU'RE HEROES, THE LOT OF YOU!

HE COULDN'T HAVE STOPPED TO PICK UP JONAS! THE BOAT WAS ALREADY OVERLOADED! JONAS MUST HAVE REALISED THAT BEFORE — BEFORE HE . . .

TOD! YOU'RE HOME — AND IN ONE PIECE!

IT'S GOOD TO BE HOME, MUM. ER — SKIP TEA, PLEASE — I'M NOT HUNGRY.

IN THE PRIVACY OF HIS OWN ROOM THE EVENTS OF THE PAST FEW DAYS CAUGHT UP WITH TOD.

FIRST JACK — NOW JONAS . . .

THEN A COUPLE OF MONTHS AFTER DUNKIRK ANOTHER SYMPATHY CARD ARRIVED.

IT'S FROM JONAS! HE'S ALIVE!

Yes! I made it! No thanks to you. Guess I was luckier than Jack. Oneday! Tod. J.K.

RELIEF AT JONAS' SURVIVAL WAS IMMEDIATE THEN TOD KNEW WHAT HE HAD TO DO.

I'VE GOT TO FIND JONAS, MUM. I'VE GOT TO PUT THE RECORD STRAIGHT.

BE CAREFUL, SON. LOOK AFTER YOURSELF.

BUT IN GAULSEA, HIS OLD HOME-TOWN . . .

THE THOMASES, THE HUNTERS, THE KYLES — ALL BOMBED OUT, TOD. MIND YOU, JONAS WASN'T HERE AT THE TIME. I HEARD SAY HE'D JOINED UP.

IN OCTOBER, 1940, TOD JOINED THE ROYAL NAVY AS AN ORDINARY SEAMAN.

MY OLD MAN SAYS IT'LL ALL BE OVER SOON, MATE. I'M KEN NOLAN — MOST FOLK CALL ME GINGER.

HI, THERE. I'M TOD GRAHAM.

DURING THE MONTHS THAT FOLLOWED TOD WAS ABLE TO PUSH THOUGHTS OF JONAS TO THE BACK OF HIS MIND AS HE MADE NEW FRIENDS.

JOIN THE NAVY AND SEE THE WORLD? SOME HOPE! I'D HAVE JOINED THE ARMY IF I'D KNOWN!

SWING THOSE ARMS! STOP TALKING IN THE RANKS!

WATCH IT, GINGER!

43

AFTER COMPLETING BASIC TRAINING TOD VOLUNTEERED FOR THE NAVAL COMMANDOS.

ROYAL NAVAL COMMANDOS? ARE YOU CRAZY, TOD? THAT'S A DANGEROUS OUTFIT TO BE IN!

SO THEY TELL ME, GINGER.

TOD WAS TURNED DOWN, AS WAS HIS REQUEST TO JOIN THE SUBMARINE SERVICE.

COMMANDOS, SUBS — YOU MUST BE OUT OF YOUR MIND, TOD! WE'VE GOT A RIGHT CUSHY NUMBER HERE! ARE YOU TRYING TO PROVE SOMETHING?

MAYBE, GINGER. I JUST WANT TO GET IN ON THE ACTION.

YOU COWARD! YOU LOUSY COWARD!

YES, TOD WAS TRYING TO PROVE SOMETHING — IF ONLY TO HIMSELF.

THEN IN JANUARY, 1942, TOD AND GEORGE WERE POSTED TO H.M.S. SUNDOWN, A CONVOY ESCORT CORVETTE.

ATLANTIC CONVOYS — IN MID-WINTER, TOO! YOU WISHED THIS ON US, TOD!

STOP GRIPING, GINGER! IT'S BETTER THAN WHITEWASHING ROTTEN PAVING STONES!

TOD WOULD NEVER FORGET THAT MOMENT ABOARD THE SUNDOWN WHEN THE SKIPPER INTRODUCED HIMSELF.

I AM YOUR CAPTAIN, LIEUTENANT – COMMANDER FRASER, AND THIS IS MY NUMBER ONE, SUB-LIEUTENANT KYLE.

JONAS!

JONAS DIDN'T SPEAK AS HE SAW TOD BUT HIS EYES SHOWED HATE AND CONTEMPT.

A HAPPY SHIP IS AN EFFICIENT SHIP, MEN. WE HAVE A DIFFICULT JOB TO DO AND WE ARE GOING TO DO IT TOGETHER.

IT WAS FATE. FOR SOME UNEARTHLY REASON IT SEEMED TOD AND JONAS WERE DESTINED TO MEET UP NO MATTER WHAT THE CIRCUMSTANCES.

WHAT'S UP, TOD? YOU LOOK LIKE YOU'VE SEEN A GHOST.

SORT OF, GINGER.

44

DURING THE NEXT FEW DAYS, AS THE SUNDOWN TOOK ON STORES AND AMMO, JONAS KEPT HIS DISTANCE. IT WAS ALMOST AS IF HE HAD DECIDED TO IGNORE TOD.

TAKE HER UP! LOOK LIVELY NOW!

WHAT GAME'S JONAS PLAYING? HE'S GOT TO SPEAK TO ME SOME TIME.

THEN AS THE SUNDOWN SAILED TO TAKE UP ESCORT DUTY . . .

ABLE SEAMAN GRAHAM — REPORT TO THE BRIDGE!

CUT, TOD . . . HEY, THE DEATH CARD!

NOW WHAT HAVE I DONE?

JONAS WAS ALONE ON THE BRIDGE. FOR SEVERAL TENSE MOMENTS HE REMAINED SILENT, HIS BACK TO TOD.

JONAS? I — I TRIED TO FIND YOU. I WAS TOLD YOU'D JOINED UP. I — I SHOULD HAVE REALISED YOU'D GO FOR A COMMISSION. YOU ALWAYS WERE THE BRAINY ONE.

WHEN JONAS TURNED, TOD SAW THE HATRED IN HIS EYES.

ABOUT WHAT HAPPENED, JONAS . . .

SIR! YOU CALL ME SIR! AND I KNOW WHAT HAPPENED! YOU LEFT MY BROTHER TO DIE! YOU LEFT ME TO DIE, BUT I'M STILL HERE. I'M GOING TO PROVE TO THE WORLD WHAT A SNIVELLING COWARD YOU ARE!

TOD KNEW THERE WAS NO USE ARGUING WITH JONAS. HIS MIND HAD BEEN POISONED WITH YEARS OF BROODING HATRED.

YOUR ACTION STATION WILL BE BRIDGE PHONES, GRAHAM — RIGHT UP HERE BESIDE ME! DISMISS!

AYE-AYE, SIR!

EVERYTHING ALL RIGHT, NUMBER ONE?

AT DAWN . . .

ACTION STATIONS! ACTION STATIONS!

COR, YOU'D THINK THEY'D GIVE US TIME TO SETTLE IN!

TOD REPORTED TO THE BRIDGE.

A-GUN REPORTS CLOSED UP, SIR! B-GUN CLOSED UP . . .!

ENEMY AIRCRAFT BEARING RED THREE-FIVE, SIR!

ALL GUNS ENGAGE WHEN READY!

THE ENEMY ATTACKED AND TOD DUCKED INSTINCTIVELY AS BOMBS BURST CLOSE.

HARD A-PORT, HELMSMAN!

ON YOUR FEET, GRAHAM!

JONAS' VOICE WAS LOADED WITH CONTEMPT.

OR MAYBE YOU'D LIKE TO RUN AND HIDE, SAILOR?

THE SUNDOWN TOOK A DIRECT HIT ABAFT THE BRIDGE.

TOD GRABBED A HOSE AS FLAMES SWEPT THE CHARTROOM.

FIRE, SIR!

GET IT UNDER CONTROL THEN!

HE BATTLED AGAINST THE SEARING FLAMES, AWARE ALL THE TIME THAT JONAS' EYES NEVER LEFT HIM FOR A SECOND.

BUT TOD'S COOLNESS IN ACTION HAD NOT GONE UNNOTICED, MUCH TO JONAS' ANNOYANCE.

WELL DONE, GRAHAM.

THANK YOU, SIR.

THE SUNDOWN LIMPED INTO PORT FOR REPAIRS. THERE TOD TOLD HIS TROUBLES TO GINGER.

THE MAN MUST BE SICK, TOD! HE'LL GET YOU KILLED! YOU'VE GOT TO SEE THE SKIPPER AND GET YOURSELF OFF THE SUNDOWN, AND QUICK!

RUN AWAY? JONAS WOULD LIKE THAT. IT WOULD PROVE HIS POINT. NO, I'VE GOT TO STICK IT OUT, GINGER. LET JONAS DO HIS DARNDEST. IT'S THE ONLY WAY WE CAN END THIS THING!

AFTER REPAIRS THE SUNDOWN RETURNED TO ESCORT DUTY. THROUGHOUT AN INCIDENT-FREE VOYAGE TO THE STATES, TOD COULD SENSE JONAS' SIMMERING HATRED.

KEEP A BETTER WATCH, GRAHAM. I WON'T HAVE YOU IDLE!

THEN ON THE RETURN VOYAGE WITH SHIPS PACKED WITH VITAL SUPPLIES—

IT'S THE MORNING STAR, SIR!

FULL AHEAD BOTH! STAND BY DEPTH-CHARGES!

URGED ON BY THE EVER HASTENING PING OF THE ASDIC, THE SUNDOWN SOUGHT OUT THE RAIDING U-BOAT.

SEARCH AND ATTACK FOLLOWED RELENTLESSLY UNTIL DEPTH-CHARGES BLASTED HER TO THE SURFACE.

THAR SHE BLOWS! ONE UP FOR THE SUNDOWN, LADS!

THEN—

SILVER EMPRESS REPORTS UNEXPLODED TORPEDO AMIDSHIPS, SIR!

GOOD GRIEF! AND SHE'S CARRYING AMMUNITION!

LET ME GO ABOARD, SIR. I MAY BE ABLE TO DEFUSE IT!

TOD REALISED IT WAS THE MOMENT JONAS HAD BEEN WAITING FOR.

SIGNAL SILVER EMPRESS I'M SENDING OVER A BOARDING PARTY.

I'LL JUST NEED ONE MAN, SIR. GRAHAM WILL VOLUNTEER.

HE ACCOMPANIED JONAS ACROSS TO THE SILVER EMPRESS.

WE'RE HIT IN NUMBER FOUR HOLD. I'VE PUMPED BALLAST TO LIFT IT ABOVE THE WATER-LINE.

ALL RIGHT, CAPTAIN. HAVE ALL BUT VITAL CREWMEN TAKE TO THE BOATS AND LIE OFF!

IN THE HOLD THEY WERE MET BY A FEARSOME SIGHT.

FIX THE LIGHT, THEN FIND SOMETHING TO HOLD THE TIN-FISH STEADY.

47

CONTINUED ON PAGE 65

48

Commando

AN R.A.F. HURRICANE SQUADRON, SPLIT BY RIVALRIES, TACKLES THE MIGHT OF THE LUFTWAFFE OVER WAR-TORN NORTHERN RUSSIA.

FIGHTERS NORTH

50

HEY, HOW DO I GET TO BECOME A PILOT WITH YOUR LOT?

I'M AFRAID IT TAKES A LOT OF LOLLY TO BECOME A FLIER WITH THIS SQUADRON, OLD BEAN. RATHER LIKE THE CAVALRY WE ARE . . .

THE AUXILIARY AIR FORCE HAD BEEN STARTED IN 1924 AS A RESERVE AIR FORCE. YOUNG MEN WERE RECRUITED TO FORM FIGHTER SQUADRONS OF PART-TIME FLIERS, LOCALLY-BASED TO DEFEND MAJOR CITIES OR TARGETS. JUST AS THE ARMY'S YEOMANRY REGIMENTS ATTRACTED WELL-TO-DO MEMBERS, THE AUXILIARY AIR FORCE TENDED TO APPEAL TO RECRUITS WITH MONEY AND THE ATMOSPHERE WAS MORE OF PRIVATE FLYING CLUBS THAN OPERATIONAL UNITS.

. . . KNIGHTS AND SQUIRES AND ALL THAT. PERHAPS YOU'D LIKE TO BE A MECHANIC OR A CLERK?

CLERK? GET LOST! AND YOUR SQUADRON TOO!

NICK WAS STILL SMARTING WHEN HE MET NEW TEAM MEMBER FRANK STIRLING AT HIS LOCAL AMATEUR FOOTBALL CLUB.

LOLLY! I ASK YOU, WHAT'S LOLLY TO DO WITH FLYIN'?

COOL DOWN, MATE! WHY DON'T YOU APPLY TO JOIN THE R.A.F. VOLUNTEER RESERVE LIKE ME?

THE R.A.F. VOLUNTEER RESERVE WAS STARTED IN JULY, 1936. WOULD-BE PILOTS TOOK A PART-TIME COURSE THEN FORMED A POOL OF TRAINED PERSONNEL AVAILABLE FOR AIRCREW SHOULD WAR BREAK-OUT.

I'VE JUST PASSED MY MEDICAL AT HULL. I'LL START TRAINING SOON AT AN AIRFIELD NEAR HERE.

YOU WILL? GEE, THEN THAT'S FOR ME TOO!

AND A FEW WEEKS LATER—

I'M IN! I START TRAINING NEXT WEEKEND AT LITTLE WISBY!

NICK'S FIRST FLIGHT WAS THE THRILL OF HIS LIFE AND HE WAS OVER-JOYED WHEN HIS INSTRUCTOR LET HIM TAKE THE CONTROLS.

THIS IS THE LIFE . . . BEATS CLERKING IN THAT OFFICE ALL DAY . . . EVEN FOOTBALL!

NICK WAS A NATURAL. AFTER THREE AND A HALF HOURS DUAL HE WENT SOLO — AN EXCEPTIONAL PILOT!

I WISH THAT AUXILIARY BLOKE COULD SEE ME NOW.

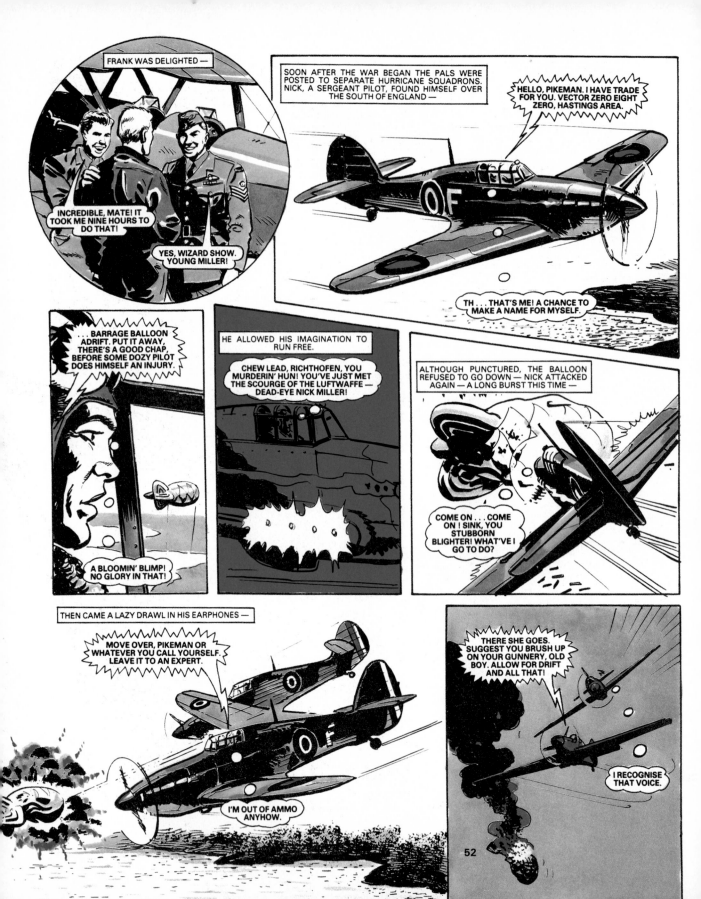

FRANK WAS DELIGHTED —

INCREDIBLE, MATE! IT TOOK ME NINE HOURS TO DO THAT!

YES, WIZARD SHOW. YOUNG MILLER!

SOON AFTER THE WAR BEGAN THE PALS WERE POSTED TO SEPARATE HURRICANE SQUADRONS. NICK, A SERGEANT PILOT, FOUND HIMSELF OVER THE SOUTH OF ENGLAND —

HELLO, PIKEMAN. I HAVE TRADE FOR YOU. VECTOR ZERO EIGHT ZERO, HASTINGS AREA.

TH . . . THAT'S ME! A CHANCE TO MAKE A NAME FOR MYSELF.

. . . BARRAGE BALLOON ADRIFT. PUT IT AWAY, THERE'S A GOOD CHAP, BEFORE SOME DOZY PILOT DOES HIMSELF AN INJURY.

A BLOOMIN' BLIMP! NO GLORY IN THAT!

HE ALLOWED HIS IMAGINATION TO RUN FREE.

CHEW LEAD, RICHTHOFEN, YOU MURDERIN' HUN! YOU'VE JUST MET THE SCOURGE OF THE LUFTWAFFE — DEAD-EYE NICK MILLER!

ALTHOUGH PUNCTURED, THE BALLOON REFUSED TO GO DOWN — NICK ATTACKED AGAIN — A LONG BURST THIS TIME —

COME ON . . . COME ON ! SINK, YOU STUBBORN BLIGHTER! WHAT'VE I GO TO DO?

THEN CAME A LAZY DRAWL IN HIS EARPHONES —

MOVE OVER, PIKEMAN OR WHATEVER YOU CALL YOURSELF. LEAVE IT TO AN EXPERT.

I'M OUT OF AMMO ANYHOW.

THERE SHE GOES. SUGGEST YOU BRUSH UP ON YOUR GUNNERY, OLD BOY. ALLOW FOR DRIFT AND ALL THAT!

I RECOGNISE THAT VOICE.

NICK'S HUMILIATION WAS COMPLETE WHEN HE RETURNED TO BASE. THE OTHER PILOT HAD LANDED AHEAD OF HIM —

WHAT'S THE RAF COMING TO? COULDN'T HIT A BARN DOOR WITH A PIKESTAFF!

REALLY? A DEFENCELESS BALLOON?

THE AUXILIARY BLOKE! HE RECOGNISES ME. I'M A LAUGHING STOCK!

A FEW DAYS LATER HE HAD TO REPORT SICK.

MEASLES! BUT THE SQUADRON LEAVES FOR FRANCE IN A DAY OR TWO!

SORRY, OLD BOY. MUST KEEP YOU IN QUARANTINE!

AND SO —

DON'T WORRY, OLD SON! WE'LL LEAVE SOME BALLOONS FOR YOU TO SHOOT DOWN!

AW, GET LOST!

NICK WASN'T TOO DISAPPOINTED TO BE POSTED TO A NEW SQUADRON IN YORKSHIRE. AFTER INTENSIVE TRAINING THEY MOVED BACK SOUTH DURING THE BATTLE OF BRITAIN —

HURRICANES TAKE THE BOMBERS . . . DIVE, DIVE, GO!

THIS IS IT! FIRST TASTE OF ACTION!

NICK'S STOMACH CHURNED AS THE ANT-LIKE SPECKS HURTLED TOWARDS HIM AT A FRIGHTENING SPEED, LIGHTS WINKING AND FLASHING FROM THE HUMPED SHAPES OF THEIR TURRETS. THEN —

WE'RE GONNA COLLIDE!

THEN MIRACULOUSLY —

I'M THROUGH! HIT ONE OF THEM . . . SURE I DID!

53

BUT THERE WAS NO TIME TO WONDER!

BREAK! BREAK! YELLOW TWO!

WHAT'S THAT?

WHAT DO I DO TO GET THIS HUN OFF MY TAIL? THINK, MILLER! THINK!

UPWARDS SPIRAL!

THEN CAME A STALL TURN — DIVING — THROTTLE WIDE —

LOST HIM!

SUDDENLY —

HE'S AHEAD OF ME! MUST BE CHRISTMAS!

GOT HIM! MY FIRST SURE KILL!

WHEN HE LANDED —

WELL DONE, MILLER! YOU'LL BE OKAY.

THANK YOU, SIR . . . TOUCH OF THE TREMBLES.

SEPTEMBER, 1941 — THEY NEARED THE RUSSIAN COAST BUT GERMAN U-BOATS, SURFACE RAIDERS AND BOMBERS DID THEIR BEST TO STOP THEM GETTING THERE!

NOT A LOT OF ROOM TO GET OFF. THE NAVY BOYS SAID TO GIVE IT FULL THROTTLE.

ALL THE HURRICANES GOT OFF, BUT AS THEY APPROACHED THEIR NEW AIRFIELD —

TROIKA SQUADRON, MAKE THIS GOOD. I WANT TO IMPRESS THE RUSKIES. WE'LL LAND IN VICS OF THREE!

YELLOW THREE . . . UNDERCART MALFUNCTION! BREAKING FORMATION . . . HOPE TO SHAKE IT DOWN.

NICK COULDN'T SHAKE HIS WHEELS DOWN AND —

DOWN — BUT NOT IN ONE PIECE!

MILLER! TRUST YOU TO SPOIL THE WHOLE SHOW!

YOU'D THINK I BENT HER DELIBERATELY!

THANKS TO A SHORTAGE OF SUPPLIES, ALL SORTS OF SNARL-UPS CROPPED UP.

BLUE TWO, DO YOU READ ME?

BLUE TWO . . . I . . . FEEL LIGHT-HEADED . . .

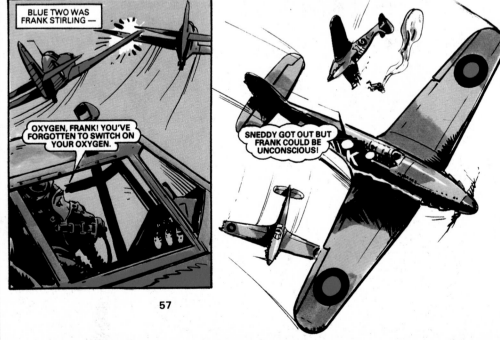

BLUE TWO WAS FRANK STIRLING —

OXYGEN, FRANK! YOU'VE FORGOTTEN TO SWITCH ON YOUR OXYGEN.

SNEDDY GOT OUT BUT FRANK COULD BE UNCONSCIOUS!

AT THE LAST SECOND FRANK PULLED OUT —

I'M OKAY, NICK! I'LL MAKE IT BACK

KEEP AN EYE ON THAT OXYGEN IN FUTURE, MATE!

OXYGEN IS ON, NICK! THERE'S A FAULT IN THE SYSTEM!

YOU'D BETTER RETURN TO BASE. WE'LL RESUME OUR PATROL.

IN TIME THEY CAME UPON A LONE GERMAN BOMBER.

TALLY-HO! WE'VE GOT HIM COLD!

AS NICK CLOSED IN FOR THE KILL, THE GERMAN TOP-GUNNER OPENED UP —

MY GUNS ARE JAMMED! AND I'M HIT!

I'D HAVE NAILED THE BOMBER FOR SURE! BUT JOE'LL GET HIM!

BUT THE GERMAN GUNNER WAS ON TARGET —

NO! THAT GUNNER WOULD'VE BEEN DEAD IF MY GUNS HADN'T JAMMED.

NICK SEETHED WITH FRUSTRATION —

DRAT THIS SMOKE! I CAN'T SEE A THING!

WHAT A FIASCO! THREE HURRICANES LOST AND NOT A SINGLE VICTORY! THE RUSKIES WON'T THINK MUCH OF *THAT*!

BACK AT BASE, NICK COMPLAINED ABOUT THE STATE OF THE EQUIPMENT —

I CAN DO NOTHING, SERGEANT! OUR SUPPLIES ARE STUCK DOWN THE LINE AND IF YOU THINK I'M SPENDING ALL MY TIME PLEADING WITH A BUNCH OF SMELLY RUSSIAN PEASANTS YOU'RE MISTAKEN!

THEN THE SERGEANTS WILL HAVE TO DO SOMETHING ABOUT IT!

BACK IN THE SERGEANTS' MESS —

RIGHT, YOU LOT! ALL YOUR SPARE FAGS, CHOCOLATE AND TINNED EATS IN THERE!

CHOCOLATE? I ONLY GOT ONE BAR! DON'T KNOW WHEN WE'LL GET ANOTHER RATION!

AN HOUR LATER, AT A NEARBY RUSSIAN FIGHTER STATION —

NICK AND FRANK GAVE A HAIR RAISING DISPLAY OF AEROBATICS.

IS TOP CLASS FLYING, COMRADES. YOU BRING GIFTS AS WELL!

GIFTS? WELL — THINK OF IT AS MORE OF A SWAP . . .

AN HOUR LATER —

YOU WILL GET YOUR THINGS, TOVARICH! I, LEO YEMOLSKY, ENGINEERING OFFICER, WILL SEE TO IT PERSONALLY.

TA! NICK MILLER'S THE NAME.

TWO DAYS LATER, TWO RUSSIAN TRUCKS ROLLED ON TO THE AIRFIELD —

HEY, WHERE NICKEE MILLER? I BRING HIM TOOLS AND SPARES!

MILLER? I AM SNEDDY, THE COMMANDING OFFICER HERE!

SNEDDY! YOU ARE STUCK-UP ONE WHO SHOUTS ON TELEPHONE. I NOT DEAL WITH YOU!

HEY, NICK, IT'S OUR STUFF!

IMMEDIATELY, THE RUSSIANS' SPARES WERE UNPACKED AND PUT TO GOOD USE.

SO YOU CRAWLED TO THE RUSSIANS, MILLER?

YEH, I'D HAVE CRAWLED TO OLD NICK HIMSELF FOR THAT LOT, SNEDDY. IT SHOULD'VE BEEN YOUR JOB.

UPSTART SEARGEANT! I'LL TEACH HIM TO SPEAK TO ME LIKE THAT!

BACK AT BASE THE RUSSIANS LAID ON A HEROES' WELCOME.

OUR COMMANDER, MAJOR-GENERAL JAROLSKI, SENDS HIS CONGRATULATIONS.

IT WAS DUE MAINLY TO THE PARTS YOU BROUGHT, LEO!

AS THE DAYS PASSED, NICK'S TALLY GRADUALLY MOUNTED—

GOOD SHOW, NICK! YOU'RE ONLY ONE BEHIND THAT TWERP, SNEDDY!

THANKS, MATE!

SNEDDY OVERHEARD THE RADIO CONVERSATION AND WAS FURIOUS...

WHO SAID THAT? I'LL HAVE THAT MAN!

PHRRRUUUUT!

...AND BECAME EVEN MORE SO WHEN SOMEONE BLEW A RASPBERRY!

SNEDDY AND THE AUXILIARY OFFICERS STILL SAW THE WAR AS A BIT OF A GAME AND WERE CONTEMPTUOUS OF THE SERGEANTS' MORE PROFESSIONAL AND RUTHLESS ATTITUDE.

CAN'T HAVE A SHOWER OF UNCOUTH SERGEANTS SHOWING US UP. I'LL HAVE TO DO SOMETHING ABOUT IT.

SNEDDY SAW NICK AS HIS BIGGEST THREAT AS LEADER AND TOOK HIM OFF FLYING DUTIES.

...SO I'VE APPOINTED YOU TO LIAISON DUTIES WITH THE RUSSIANS AS YOU GET ON SO WELL.

B...BUT...

TWO BIRDS WITH ONE STONE! GOT RID OF THAT TROUBLEMAKER... AND ELIMINATED THE THREAT TO MY RECORD AT THE SAME TIME.

A FEW DAYS LATER SNEDDY HAD ANOTHER "KILL"—

AN UNARMED OBSERVER... BUT IT STILL COUNTS.

I'VE NO INTENTION OF GETTING MY TAIL SHOT OFF FOR MOTHER RUSSIA.

THE ENCROACHING RUSSIAN WINTER WITH ITS BRIEF HOURS OF DAYLIGHT HAD NOT ONLY INCREASED SNEDDY'S DISLIKE FOR THE COUNTRY, BUT SAPPED HIS WILL TO FIGHT FOR IT. HE HAD RESOLVED TO STICK HIS NECK OUT NO MORE THAN WAS STRICTLY NECESSARY.

IN SPITE OF SNEDDY THE SQUADRON'S RECORD WAS GOOD. ONE DAY AT RUSSIAN H.Q. —

SERGEANT MILLER, YOUR SQUADRON WILL ESCORT MAJOR-GENERAL JAROLSKI ON A FLIGHT TO BATTLEFRONT.

GREAT, COLONEL. UNFORTUNATELY I'LL BE STUCK HERE AT H.Q.

A FELLOW SERGEANT WAS SOON IN TROUBLE.

BREAK, TINY! BREAK!

AW, NO! TOO LATE!

THE HUN ROLLED ON TO HIS BACK AND DROPPED FOR THE CLOUD —

YOU WON'T GET AWAY THAT WAY, FRITZ!

PHEW! ALMOST COLLIDED! THAT'S SNEDDY!

I'LL COVER THE TRANSPORT! GO AFTER THAT JOKER, MILLER!

BUT —

MORE JERRIES . . . AND SNEDDY'S RUNNING FOR IT!

I'M NOT RISKING MY NECK FOR SOME THICK RUSSIAN GENERAL!

FRANK'S HURRICANE SCREAMED ALONGSIDE.

SOMEBODY'S DUCKED OUT, NICK!

OUR BELOVED C.O! WE'VE GOT TO INTERCEPT THOSE HUNS BEFORE THEY REACH THE TRANSPORT!

A BURST AT MAXIMUM RANGE MIGHT PUT THE WIND UP THEM!

BLIMEY, DEAD-EYE DICK! YOU'VE EQUALLED SNEDDY'S SCORE.

63

GET THAT BLIGHTER BREAKING RIGHT, FRANK. I'LL GET THE OTHER.

NICK SWUNG IN HARD BEHIND THE ENEMY FIGHTER. HE STEADIED THE GUNSIGHT ON HIS TARGET, BUT WHEN HE PRESSED THE BUTTON —

BLAST! OUT OF AMMO!

NICK DIDN'T HESITATE —

PHEW! YOU COULD CALL THAT IN THE "NICK" OF TIME.

NICK MADE IT BACK TO BASE — JUST.

YOU ARE A CREDIT TO YOUR COUNTRY AND YOUR SQUADRON, SERGEANT. I SHALL SEE YOU RECEIVE OUR HIGHEST HONOUR.

ALTHOUGH SNEDDY PRETENDED HIS AIRCRAFT HAD DEVELOPED ENGINE TROUBLE, NOBODY BELIEVED HIM. SOON AFTERWARDS HE WAS QUIETLY SENT HOME. NICK MILLER WAS AWARDED THE D.F.M.. TROIKA SQUADRON WENT ON FROM SUCCESS TO SUCCESS.

IT WAS JUST PART OF THE JOB, LEO!

THE END

THE COWARD
CONTINUED FROM PAGE 48

AS THE SUNDOWN BATTLED AGAINST THE NORTH ATLANTIC, AND THE EVER-PRESENT U-BOAT WOLF PACKS, JONAS SEIZED UPON EVERY OPPORTUNITY TO WAGE HIS OWN PRIVATE WAR.

DO YOU SLEEP NIGHTS, TOD? DO YOU SEE JACK THERE IN THE WATER CALLING OUT TO YOU?

IT WASN'T LIKE THAT—SIR!

TOD HAD TRIED TO TELL JONAS WHAT HAD REALLY HAPPENED THE DAY THE WANDERLUST CAPSIZED, BUT JONAS HAD TOD MARKED AS A COWARD WHO HAD LEFT HIS TWIN BROTHER TO DIE AND THERE WAS NO HOLDING HIM.

NEW YORK, TOD. A GOOD PLACE TO GET OUT OF THE WAR FOR SOME COWARDLY CUR WHO FEELS HE'S HAD ENOUGH.

IT WAS ALMOST AN INVITATION . . .

. . . AND ONE WHICH TOD CAME CLOSE TO CONSIDERING DURING A LOW MOMENT ASHORE.

JUMP SHIP? YOU CAN'T DO IT, TOD! YOU'D BE PLAYING INTO HIS HANDS!

YES, WOULDN'T I JUST. HE'D LOVE TO SEE ME DRAGGED BACK ON BOARD IN CHAINS, A DESERTER, A COWARD! TROUBLE IS, I'M NOT SURE I CAN TAKE MUCH MORE, GINGER.

THEN, ON THE RETURN TRIP—

ASDIC REPORTS ECHO BEARING GREEN 35, SIR — RANGE 1,500 YARDS AND CLOSING!

STARBOARD TEN! STAND BY DEPTH-CHARGES!

WITH WELL-PRACTISED SKILL THE SUNDOWN LAID ITS PATTERN OF DEATH . . .

AS THE SUNDOWN WENT INTO THE ATTACK, THE FIRST OF THE U-BOAT'S TORPEDOES CLAIMED ITS TARGET CLOSE BY.

. . . FORCING THE U-BOAT TO THE SURFACE.

U-BOAT ON SURFACE, SIR!

HARD A STARBOARD! STAND BY TO RAM!

ALL HANDS BRACE FOR IMPACT!

U 151

WITH A GRINDING AND TEARING OF METAL THE SUNDOWN STRUCK HOME.

U-151

THE HOLE IN THE U-BOAT'S SIDE WAS FATAL AND IT WAS OBVIOUS SHE HAD CEASED TO BE A FIGHTING MACHINE.

FULL ASTERN BOTH! STAND BY TO PICK UP SURVIVORS!

U-151

BUT AS THE ENGINES THROBBED AND THE SUNDOWN'S HULL GROANED IN PROTEST, HER BOW REMAINED LOCKED IN THE STRICKEN U-BOAT'S HULL.

WE'RE TAKING HER WITH US, SIR! WE'VE JAMMED!

HALTED, THE SUNDOWN WOULD BECOME A SITTING DUCK FOR ANY OTHER LURKING U-BOAT.

STOP ENGINES!

WE'LL HAVE TO CUT HER FREE, SIR! COME WITH ME, GRAHAM!

AYE, AYE — SIR!

PETTY OFFICER YATES HAD VOLUNTEERED TO JOIN JONAS AND TOD ON THE SUB.

MOVE IT! WE CAN'T STAY AROUND HERE ALL DAY!

HOLD THOSE CYLINDERS STEADY, GRAHAM!

FUEL ON THE WATER, SIR!

GOOD GRIEF! SWITCH OFF, YATES!

IT WAS TOO LATE. A SEA OF FLAME FLARED UP AND SURROUNDED TOD.

AAARGH!

TOD'S LINE WAS SEVERED. AS HE STRUGGLED IN THE BLAZING WATER, HIS CRY FOR HELP WENT UNHEEDED BY JONAS.

GET THEM UP!

HELP ME!

AS JONAS WAS HAULED TO SAFETY, IT WAS P.O. YATES WHO CAME TO THE RESCUE.

HAUL AWAY!

RELUCTANTLY THE SUNDOWN FREED HERSELF FROM THE STRICKEN U-BOAT.

U151

TOD AND P.O. YATES WERE TREATED FOR BURNS.

GLAD YOU WERE AROUND, P.O. I'M IN YOUR DEBT.

YOU'D HAVE DONE THE SAME FOR ME, TOD — I HOPE.

FOR THE REMAINDER OF THE VOYAGE JONAS SEEMED STRANGELY SUBDUED. HE HARDLY SPOKE TO TOD AND AVOIDED BEING ALONE WITH HIM WHENEVER POSSIBLE. WOULD HE HAVE DELIBERATELY LET TOD DIE HAD NOT P.O. YATES COME TO THE RESCUE?

DO YOU FEEL BETTER NOW, JONAS? ARE WE EVEN?

TOD COULD SENSE HIS ONE-TIME FRIEND WAS BATTLING WITH HIS CONSCIENCE.

OR HAVE I GOT TO DIE BEFORE YOU STOP TORTURING YOURSELF?

SHUT UP! DO YOU HEAR? SHUT UP!

67

ACTION STATIONS! ACTION STATIONS!

IF YOU THOUGHT THE ATLANTIC WAS GRIM, MATES, YOU AIN'T SEEN NOTHIN' YET!

IN JUNE, 1942, THE SUNDOWN WAS SWITCHED TO ARCTIC CONVOY DUTY.

THE CONVOY WAS ABLE TO KEEP BEYOND THE RANGE OF NORWEGIAN-BASED ENEMY BOMBERS UNTIL IT WAS FORCED TO TURN EAST PAST BEAR ISLAND . . .

ENEMY AIRCRAFT BEARING GREEN 25, SIR!

ALL GUNS ENGAGE WHEN READY!

THE MASSED BOMBER FORMATIONS TOOK A TERRIBLE TOLL.

ONE OF THE CASUALTIES WAS THE SUNDOWN AND WITHIN MINUTES SHE WAS LISTING BADLY.

THEN CAME THE DREADED ORDER—

ABANDON SHIP!

LEAVE ME! I — I'VE HAD IT, TOD!

NO WAY, JONAS! ON YOUR FEET!

TOD DRAGGED JONAS INTO THE ICY WATER, WHERE A MAN WAS GIVEN BUT TWO MINUTES TO LIVE.

WE CAN MAKE IT, JONAS! WE CAN MAKE IT!

FIGHTING THE MIND-NUMBING COLD AND HIS OWN WOUNDS, TOD HAULED JONAS ABOARD A RAFT.

LEAVE ME . . . LEAVE ME . . .

KEEP AWAKE, JONAS! KEEP AWAKE, MAN!

TOD SHOOK JONAS INTO CONSCIOUSNESS.

YOU CAN'T DIE, MAN! YOU'VE GOT TO GET EVEN! SAY IT! *SAY IT!*

GOT . . . GOT TO GET . . . EVEN!

MINUTES SEEMED LIKE HOURS AS THE BITTER COLD BIT DEEPLY INTO EVERY MUSCLE.

GOT TO GET EVEN WITH THE COWARD . . . HE LET JACK DIE . . . LET JACK DIE . . . I SAY IT, JONAS! SAY IT!

LET JACK DIE . . .

TOD CAME TO IN SICK BAY ABOARD THE RESCUING DESTROYER.

SUB-LIEUTENANT KYLE — DID HE MAKE IT?

COULDN'T TELL YOU, MATE. A LOT OF THEM DIDN'T.

TOD WAS KEPT IN A BASE HOSPITAL AT SCAPA FLOW FOR SEVERAL WEEKS. THEN ONE AFTERNOON HE HAD A VISITOR.

YOU TOOK SOME FINDING, TOD. SOMEBODY TOLD ME THEY'D LEFT YOU IN ARCHANGEL.

JONAS!

I HEARD WHAT YOU DID TO SAVE ME. I WAS WRONG ABOUT YOU AND JACK — AND ME. YOU'RE NO COWARD.

TOD CLASPED JONAS' HAND EAGERLY AND THE BITTER YEARS SEEMED TO ROLL AWAY.

IT'S OVER, JONAS — ALL OVER. LET'S MAKE UP FOR ALL THOSE WASTED YEARS. IT COULD BE A LONG WAR, BUT WE'LL BE ON THE SAME SIDE THIS TIME.

THE END

Commando

"LOOK AFTER NUMBER ONE" HAD ALWAYS BEEN DANIEL CONWAY'S MOTTO. YET HERE HE WAS ABOUT TO TACKLE A TIGER TANK SINGLE-HANDED.

RELUCTANT HERO

WARTIME SPECIAL RAIDING FORCES WERE VOLUNTEERS, BUT NOT EVERY RAIDER WANTED TO BE IN THE THICK OF THE ACTION — AND IT DIDN'T HELP IF YOU CAME FROM A FAMILY WITH A MILITARY TRADITION. DANIEL CONWAY WAS ONE SUCH RELUCTANT VOLUNTEER . . .

1936 — EIGHTEEN YEAR OLD DANIEL CONWAY, HOME FROM BOARDING SCHOOL FOR THE HOLIDAYS, WAS GIVING HIS HOME-MADE SCRAMBLE CAR A TRIAL RUN.

AND LOUIS MEYER COMES THROUGH ON THE INSIDE TO TAKE THE LEAD IN THE INDIANAPOLIS 500 WITH A LAP RECORD! THERE'S NO ONE TO CATCH HIM NOW!

DANIEL'S FATHER, MAJOR CHARLES CONWAY, HAD TAKEN LEAVE FROM HIS REGIMENT TO VISIT HIS SON.

WHAT THE BLUE BLAZES!

LOOK OUT!

MAJOR CONWAY HAD LITTLE TIME FOR DANIEL'S OUT-OF-SCHOOL ACTIVITIES AND IT WAS NOT A MEETING DANIEL WAS LOOKING FORWARD TO.

WHAT ON EARTH DO YOU THINK YOU ARE DOING, BOY? AND WHAT IS THAT CONTRAPTION?

MY CONWAY LION, FATHER. I BUILT IT MYSELF FROM SCRAP PARTS.

71

SCRAP PARTS, INDEED! GET RID OF IT, SIMMS! AND YOU, BOY, WASH AND REPORT TO ME IN MY STUDY!

BUT DANIEL WAS NOT COWED EASILY, A TRAIT THE MAJOR RECKONED COULD GET OUT OF HAND.

SIMMS, LAY SO MUCH AS A HAND ON MY MACHINE, AND I'LL LET DOWN YOUR TYRES AND PUT SUGAR IN YOUR PETROL!

BUT IT WAS THE MAJOR'S ORDER, MASTER DANIEL.

IT'S TIME MY FATHER LEARNED THAT WE'RE NOT ALL HIS LITTLE TIN SOLDIERS, READY AND WILLING TO JUMP AT HIS EVERY COMMAND.

BUT EVEN AS HE SPOKE THE WORDS OF DEFIANCE DANIEL THOUGHT UNEASILY OF THE COMING INTERVIEW WITH HIS FATHER.

ALTHOUGH DANIEL PROLONGED CLEANING UP, THE TIME CAME WHEN HE HAD TO FACE HIS FATHER IN HIS STUDY.

WELL, LET'S HAVE IT, BOY! SIT DOWN.

MY SCHOOL REPORT, FATHER. SIGNED, SEALED AND DELIVERED.

IT HAD BEEN A TWICE-YEARLY RITUAL SINCE HE HAD ENROLLED AT BEECH MOUNT, HIS FATHER'S OLD SCHOOL.

HAVE YOU MADE THE RUGGER FIRST TEAM YET, BOY? I WAS CAPTAIN FOR THREE CONSECUTIVE YEARS. WELL, SIT UP, BOY — DON'T SLOUCH.

I'VE BEEN EXCUSED RUGGER — ON ACCOUNT OF A BACK STRAIN, FATHER.

THIS TERM DANIEL WAS SURE HIS FATHER WOULD BE FAVOURABLY IMPRESSED.

NOT BAD AT ALL, MY BOY — IN FACT YOU'VE DONE RATHER WELL. WHEN I BUMPED INTO OLD SEDGECLIFFE, HE GAVE ME THE DISTINCT IMPRESSION YOU WERE NOT LIVING UP TO THE CONWAY NAME.

YOU — YOU SAW THE HEADMASTER IN LONDON, FATHER?

DANIEL TRIED TO CONTROL HIS PANIC AS HE SAW HIS FATHER'S MOUNTING ANGER.

CONFOUND THE MAN! HE'S DONE YOU AN INJUSTICE! I SHALL GIVE HIM A PIECE OF MY MIND!

I — I WOULDN'T PHONE MR SEDGECLIFFE, FATHER. HE — HE'S GONE AWAY ON HOLIDAY.

MAJOR CONWAY WAS SUMMONED TO THE SCHOOL.

MAJOR CONWAY, I HAVE NO ALTERNATIVE BUT TO EXPEL DANIEL! SNEAKING OUT AT DEAD OF NIGHT TO GAMBLE WITH A BUNCH OF UNSAVOURY CHARACTERS!

MR SEDGECLIFFE, I IMPLORE YOU! THINK OF THE SCANDAL! THINK OF MY GOOD NAME — AND THAT OF THE SCHOOL.

THE MAJOR TALKED FOR SOME TIME AND AN ARRANGEMENT WAS AGREED. AFTERWARDS —

YOU'LL START BEHAVING LIKE A RESPONSIBLE PERSON FROM NOW ON, BOY, OR I'LL WASH MY HANDS OF YOU.

YES, FATHER.

DANIEL APPARENTLY SETTLED DOWN FOR A YEAR'S HARD WORK, THEN IN JULY, 1938, DURING THE SCHOOL ANNUAL BALL —

BEECH MOUNT SCHOOL GRAND BALL

PARK YOUR CAR, SIR?

A NEW SERVICE! GOOD IDEA! THANK YOU, YOUNG MAN.

MOMENTS LATER —

CARE FOR A JAUNT, GEORGE? THIS IS THE ONE FOR ME. COME ON, GET IN!

DO YOU THINK WE SHOULD, DANIEL?

BUT THERE WAS A BIG DIFFERENCE IN POWER BETWEEN DANIEL'S SCRAMBLE CAR AND THE MACHINE HE NOW DROVE.

DANIEL, LOOK OUT!

DANIEL ASSURED GEORGE THEY'D HAVE THE CAR BACK IN THE PARK IN NO TIME.

THE INDIANAPOLIS 500, GEORGE! WHAT I'D GIVE TO BE THERE!

HEY, SLOW DOWN, OLD CHAP!

DANIEL BRAKED DESPERATELY, BUT THE CAR SKIDDED OUT OF CONTROL.

DANIEL AND GEORGE WERE LUCKY TO ESCAPE SERIOUS INJURY, BUT THE CAR WAS A WRITE-OFF.

YOU COULD HAVE KILLED YOURSELF AND YOUR FRIEND! YOU WERE STUPID AND IRRESPONSIBLE. I WARNED YOU ABOUT YOUR CONDUCT AND YOU MUST TAKE THE CONSEQUENCES.

I'VE NO DOUBT YOU HAVE SOMETHING NASTY IN MIND FOR ME, FATHER.

AFTER DANIEL WAS DISCHARGED FROM THE HOSPITAL . . .

I'VE HAD TO PULL SOME STRINGS TO GET THIS WHOLE SORRY BUSINESS HUSHED UP! YOU ARE TO JOIN THE FARNMOUTH MILITARY COLLEGE AT THE END OF THE MONTH, WHERE PERHAPS THEY CAN MAKE A MAN OF YOU.

NO, FATHER! I'LL NOT GO TO YOUR PRECIOUS MILITARY COLLEGE. I'LL NOT HAVE MY LIFE MAPPED OUT FOR ME BY YOU OR ANYONE ELSE.

THERE'S GOING TO BE A WAR, DANIEL! THE COUNTRY IS GOING TO NEED MEN OF GOOD STANDING, MEN WHO CAN BE LEADERS!

I'M SURE YOU'LL COPE ADMIRABLY, FATHER. GOODBYE. I'LL KEEP IN TOUCH, MOTHER.

AT LEAST DANIEL DIDN'T STARVE. HIS GAMBLING ACQUAINTANCES FROM SOO HEE'S SOON FOUND GEORGE AND HIM A JOB — BUT OUTSIDE THE LAW. IN THE CHANNEL, JUNE, 1939 —

THIS IS THE COASTGUARD! HEAVE TO!

HANG ON TO YOUR HAT, GEORGE!

YOU'LL HAVE US ON THE ROCKS, DANIEL!

LATER —

I TOLD YOU WE COULD LOSE THEM, GEORGE. TRUST ME. HAVE I EVER LET YOU DOWN?

REPEATEDLY, OLD BOY.

DANIEL SOON DISCOVERED THAT IT WAS NOT WHAT YOU KNEW, BUT WHO YOU KNEW THAT SPELLED SUCCESS OR FAILURE IN HIS NEW EXCITING WORLD.

YOU'RE A ROBBER, DANIEL. THAT'S TWICE WHAT WE AGREED!

AND STILL CHEAP AT THE PRICE, HENRY. REMEMBER, I'M THE ONE WHO TAKES THE RISKS.

DANIEL LIVED BY HIS WITS, KEEPING ONE STEP AHEAD OF THE LAW UNTIL SEPTEMBER, 1939. THE DAY AFTER WAR WAS DECLARED —

I'M JOINING UP, DANIEL. ARMOURED CORPS. HOW ABOUT YOU?

ME? COME OFF IT, GEORGE. I'M NO HERO. BESIDES, I'VE GOT A BAD BACK FROM THAT CRASH AT BEECH MOUNT — REMEMBER?

DANIEL SPENT AN ENJOYABLE "PHONEY WAR" IN LONDON. THEN IN JUNE, 1940, HE PAID HIS MOTHER A VISIT.

HOW ARE YOU, MOTHER? THESE WILL BRIGHTEN THINGS UP FOR YOU.

SUGAR, TEA, BUTTER! DANIEL, THESE THINGS ARE GETTING DIFFICULT TO GET.

THERE WAS PLENTY TO BE HAD IF YOU HAD THE RIGHT CONTACTS — AND DANIEL KNEW THE RIGHT PEOPLE.

ASK NO QUESTIONS, GET NO LIES. NOW HOW IS FATHER? YOU SAID HE WAS WITH THE B.E.F. IN FRANCE.

YES, I'M TERRIBLY WORRIED ABOUT HIM, DANIEL. THINGS ARE GOING VERY BADLY OVER THERE.

DUNKIRK, AND IN THE SHRINKING BRITISH DEFENCE PERIMETER WAS WHAT REMAINED OF MAJOR CONWAY'S REGIMENT. NOW THE GERMANS WERE CLOSING IN.

DOWN TO THE BEACHES, MEN!

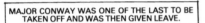

MAJOR CONWAY WAS ONE OF THE LAST TO BE TAKEN OFF AND WAS THEN GIVEN LEAVE.

OH, CHARLES, IT MUST HAVE BEEN DREADFUL!

IT DID GET A BIT STICKY, OLD GIRL. THERE'S BEEN TALK OF A PROMOTION TO LIEUTENANT-COLONEL.

MY MEN DID ME PROUD, ELIZABETH. WE'LL BE BACK AND SOON! I SAY, YOU'VE BEEN STOCKING UP, OLD GIRL . . . .

ER — JUST A LITTLE EXTRA THE GROCER LET ME HAVE, DEAR.

A COUPLE OF DAYS LATER THE MAJOR HAD A VISITOR.

JAMES, OLD BOY! HOW ARE THINGS ON THE MAGISTRATES' BENCH? I'LL BET YOU'RE BEING KEPT BUSY WITH ALL THESE NEW LAWS AND RESTRICTIONS.

YES, I AM RATHER, CHARLES. I'M AFRAID I BRING BAD NEWS.

THE MAJOR WAS TAKEN ABACK BY HIS FRIEND'S NEWS.

DANIEL HAS BEEN ARRESTED! ON WHAT CHARGE, JAMES?

BLACK MARKETEERING, CHARLES. THERE HAVE BEEN SCORES OF ARRESTS. I BELIEVE DANIEL IS ONE OF THE LITTLE FISH, BUT I THOUGHT YOU SHOULD KNOW.

MAJOR CONWAY WAS GRANTED PERMISSION TO SEE DANIEL.

SO I ERRED AND GOT CAUGHT, FATHER. I'M NOT COMPLAINING. I'LL TAKE WHAT'S COMING TO ME.

WHEN I THINK OF ALL THE BOYS YOUR AGE I WATCHED FIGHT AND DIE FOR THEIR COUNTRY, AND THEN I LOOK AT YOU, MY STOMACH CHURNS, BOY!

HOWEVER, MAJOR CONWAY TAPPED INTO THE OLD BOY NETWORK.

I KNOW I CAN'T INFLUENCE YOUR JUDGMENT, JOHN, BUT WHAT THE LAD REALLY NEEDS IS A BIT OF DISCIPLINE . . .

YOU'RE ASKING A LOT OF ME, CHARLES, BUT I'LL SEE WHAT I CAN DO.

LATER, IN COURT

SO THE OLD MAN HAS PULLED A FEW STRINGS AGAIN.

. . . AND NORMALLY I WOULD HAVE NO HESITATION IN SENTENCING YOU TO TWO YEARS IMPRISONMENT. IN THIS TIME OF CRISIS, HOWEVER, WITH OUR COUNTRY NEEDING THE SERVICES OF EDUCATED YOUNG MEN SUCH AS YOURSELF, I AM PREPARED TO POSTPONE SENTENCE TO GIVE YOU THE CHANCE TO SERVE YOUR COUNTRY . . .

THERE WAS NO GRATITUDE IN DANIEL'S VOICE AS HE CONFRONTED HIS FATHER AFTER THE HEARING.

THE ARMY OR ELSE, EH, FATHER? ALL RIGHT, WHERE IS IT TO BE?

YOU WILL REPORT TO THE ARMY RECRUITING CENTRE AT PARKVILLE, DANIEL — AND CONSIDER YOURSELF LUCKY!

MAJOR CONWAY'S INFLUENCE CARRIED NO WEIGHT IN DANIEL'S TRAINING DEPOT AND DANIEL FOUND THE TRAINING BORING, REPETITIVE AND HARD.

SWING THOSE ARMS! LEFT, RIGHT! GET YOUR HEAD UP, CONWAY!

PRISON COULDN'T HAVE BEEN ANY WORSE THAN THIS!

THEN, AFTER SIX WEEKS BASIC . . .

YOU'VE BEEN SELECTED FOR OFFICER TRAINING, CONWAY. WHY — I'LL NEVER KNOW!

SOMEONE PULLING STRINGS FROM ABOVE PERHAPS, SERGEANT?

BUT AS AN OFFICER CADET, DANIEL FOUND LIFE EVEN HARDER.

GET YOUR FEET UP, MISTER CONWAY, SIR! YOU'RE IDLE! GO ROUND AGAIN!

THERE HAS TO BE A WAY OUT OF THIS!

JUNE, 1941. NEWLY-PROMOTED LIEUTENANT-COLONEL CONWAY INVITED BRIGADIER SOAMES TO HIS HOME.

AND HOW'S THAT BOY OF YOURS GETTING ALONG, CONWAY? I HEARD HE'D GOT HIS COMMISSION.

THAT'S RIGHT, SIR! DANIEL'S REGIMENT LEFT LAST WEEK FOR NORTH AFRICA. A SPOT OF ACTION IS WHAT HE NEEDS.

CONWAY WANTED SO MUCH TO BE PROUD OF HIS SON —

HIS TEETHING TROUBLES SHOULD BE OVER — DANIEL! WHAT ARE YOU DOING HERE?

HELLO, FATHER. RECUPERATING FROM AN OLD WOUND — A SPORTS ONE.

DANIEL'S UNEXPECTED APPEARANCE CAST A BLIGHT ON HIS FATHER'S MEETING WITH THE BRIGADIER WHO SOON LEFT.

I HAVE NEVER BEEN SO HUMILIATED. IF I THOUGHT FOR ONE MOMENT YOU HAD DELIBERATELY DUCKED OUT OF SAILING WITH YOUR REGIMENT I—I . . .

COME NOW, FATHER. YOU WERE ALWAYS ON AT ME TO PLAY RUGGER. I WAS IN A GAME THE DAY BEFORE WE WERE TO EMBARK, AND THE OLD BACK WENT. I'M IN CONSTANT PAIN.

ALTHOUGH AN INFANTRY OFFICER, DANIEL WANGLED A POSTING TO AN ARMY SUPPLY DEPOT IN KENT AND FOR A YEAR HE AND A NEW FRIEND, TOBY CARSTAIRS, LED AN EASY LIFE.

THE OLD MAN'S ASKING FOR VOLUNTEERS FOR A SPECIAL MOB, DANIEL. HOW ABOUT IT? I'M FED UP HERE.

SPECIAL MOB? SOUNDS DANGEROUS, TOBY OLD SON. I'LL STAY RIGHT HERE. ARE YOU PLAYING TONIGHT? I FEEL LUCKY.

THE ONLY ACTION DANIEL WANTED TO SEE WAS AT THE CARD TABLE AND THAT NIGHT HIS LUCK CONTINUED TO HOLD.

YOUR TEN AND I'LL RAISE YOU TWENTY, GORDON.

YOU'LL TAKE AN I.O.U., DANIEL?

HIS RUN OF LUCK SEEMED UNENDING.

FOUR LOVELY ACES, GORDON. YOU WILL HONOUR THIS I.O.U., OLD BOY?

I'VE NEVER WELSHED ON A BET YET, DANIEL! YOU'LL GET YOUR MONEY!

BUT SEVERAL DAYS LATER —

GORDON'S BEEN CAUGHT FIDDLING THE MESS FUNDS, DANIEL. IF IT COMES OUT AT THE COURT-MARTIAL WHY HE NEEDED THE CASH SO DESPERATELY, WE'LL ALL BE FOR THE HIGH JUMP.

TIME WE WEREN'T HERE, TOBY. THAT SPECIAL MOB YOU MENTIONED SUDDENLY SEEMS A GOOD IDEA!

FROM HIS EASY LIFE IN THE SUPPLY DEPOT DANIEL WAS THROWN IN AT THE DEEP END IN SPECIAL RAIDING FORCES, AND SIX WEEKS LATER ON A BEACH IN CORNWALL —

RIGHT, LADS . . . FOLLOW ME!

THOSE EXPLOSIONS ARE LIKE THE REAL THING.

THEY ARE THE REAL THING, SERGEANT. LET'S HOPE THE TRAINING STAFF HAVE DONE THEIR HOMEWORK PROPERLY.

AS TRACERS WHIZZED LOW OVERHEAD, DANIEL FELT AN OLD EXCITEMENT GROW WITHIN HIM, THE SAME EXCITEMENT HE HAD FELT WHEN TRYING TO OUTWIT THE LAW.

THIS BEATS ORDINARY TRAINING EXERCISES ANY TIME.

A BATTLE-HARDENED CAPTAIN NASH HAD SET THE TRAINING EXERCISE AND GAVE HIS VERDICT.

PRAISE AT LAST! WONDER HOW TOBY GOT ON.

MAKE THAT MUCH NOISE OVER THERE, CONWAY, AND YOU'LL BE DEAD! OTHERWISE — WELL DONE.

OTHER TRAINING FOLLOWED AND DESPITE HIMSELF DANIEL FOUND HIMSELF ENJOYING THE CHALLENGE OF SOLVING THE PROBLEMS. THEN CAME THE BRIEFING FOR THE REAL THING.

LIEUTENANT JOHNSON WILL LEAD THE MAIN ASSAULT ON THE RADAR STATION. CONWAY AND CARSTAIRS WILL LEAD DIVERSIONARY RAIDS HERE AND HERE.

THEY DON'T TRUST US IN THE BIG LEAGUE, TOBY.

LATE NEXT NIGHT, OFF THE FRENCH COAST —

DANIEL COULDN'T HELP A TINGLE OF EXCITEMENT.

SO FAR SO GOOD, SIR. QUIET, ISN'T IT?

AS THE GRAVE. ALL MY INSTINCTS TELL ME WE'VE HIT . . .

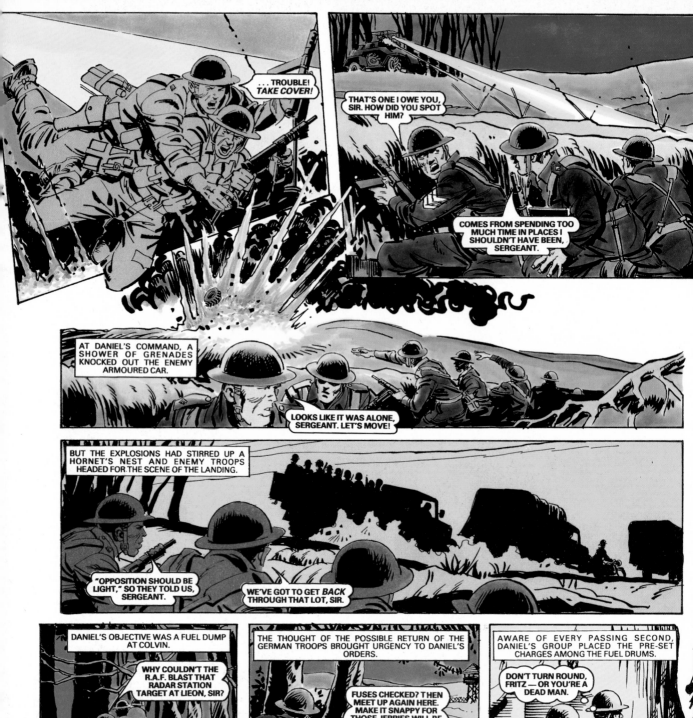

...TROUBLE! *TAKE COVER!*

THAT'S ONE I OWE YOU, SIR. HOW DID YOU SPOT HIM?

COMES FROM SPENDING TOO MUCH TIME IN PLACES I SHOULDN'T HAVE BEEN, SERGEANT.

AT DANIEL'S COMMAND, A SHOWER OF GRENADES KNOCKED OUT THE ENEMY ARMOURED CAR.

LOOKS LIKE IT WAS ALONE, SERGEANT. LET'S MOVE!

BUT THE EXPLOSIONS HAD STIRRED UP A HORNET'S NEST AND ENEMY TROOPS HEADED FOR THE SCENE OF THE LANDING.

"OPPOSITION SHOULD BE LIGHT," SO THEY TOLD US, SERGEANT.

WE'VE GOT TO GET *BACK* THROUGH THAT LOT, SIR.

DANIEL'S OBJECTIVE WAS A FUEL DUMP AT COLVIN.

WHY COULDN'T THE R.A.F. BLAST THAT RADAR STATION TARGET AT LIEON, SIR?

WE'RE GUINEA PIGS FOR THE SECOND FRONT INVASION WHEN IT COMES.

THE THOUGHT OF THE POSSIBLE RETURN OF THE GERMAN TROOPS BROUGHT URGENCY TO DANIEL'S ORDERS.

FUSES CHECKED? THEN MEET UP AGAIN HERE. MAKE IT SNAPPY FOR THOSE JERRIES WILL BE BACK ON THE DOUBLE.

AWARE OF EVERY PASSING SECOND, DANIEL'S GROUP PLACED THE PRE-SET CHARGES AMONG THE FUEL DRUMS.

DON'T TURN ROUND, FRITZ — OR YOU'RE A DEAD MAN.

THE EXPLOSIVES LAYING WENT UNDETECTED AND WITH ONLY MINUTES TO SPARE THE GROUP REASSEMBLED.

THAT'S THE LAST MAN IN, SIR.

TIME WE WEREN'T HERE.

BUT LUCK WAS AGAINST DANIEL. THE BURNING FUEL DUMP REVEALED HIS ATTACK FORCE TO THE DEFENDERS.

THAT'S TORN IT! LET'S GET OUT OF HERE.

ATTRACTED BY THE EXPLOSIONS THE GERMAN PATROL RETURNED AND DANIEL'S MEN FOUND THEMSELVES ATTACKED FROM IN FRONT AND BEHIND.

THEY'VE GOT BEHIND US, SIR!

BACK TO THE DUMP, LADS!

DANIEL HAD BEEN IN TIGHT CORNERS BEFORE AND DOING THE UNEXPECTED HAD PICKED HIM OUT OF OTHER SCRAPES.

KEEP CLOSE — AND KEEP MOVING!

WITH SURPRISE ON HIS SIDE HE HAD HALF A CHANCE.

AH — TRANSPORT!

HIS MEN FOLLOWED HIM THROUGH THE SEARING HEAT.

GET THEM ABOARD, SERGEANT!

AS DANIEL STEPPED ON THE ACCELERATOR, HE COULDN'T HELP THINKING OF THE PAST.

EVER FANCIED ENTERING THE INDIANAPOLIS 500, SERGEANT!

THE INDY — WHAT, SIR?

THE DUMP GATES WERE MEANT TO KEEP INTRUDERS OUT — NOT A RAMPAGING TRUCK IN.

WHERE THE BLAZES IS HE TAKING US?

WHO CARES? JUST HANG ON!

DANIEL KNEW THE ROAD TO THE COAST WOULD BE BLOCKED BUT THEY HAD TO REACH THEIR ESCAPE RENDEZVOUS POINT.

IT WAS TEN MINUTES SHORT OF THE PICK-UP TIME WHEN THEY REACHED THE CLIFFS SOUTH OF THE RENDEZVOUS.

ENEMY TROOPS BELOW, SIR!

WE CAN'T HANDLE THAT LOT, SIR!

IGNORE THEM! GET THE MEN DOWN TO THE BEACH, SERGEANT!

WITH HIS MEN OFF-LOADED DANIEL SET THE TRUCK ROLLING DOWN THE HILL.

INDIANAPOLIS WAS NEVER LIKE THIS!

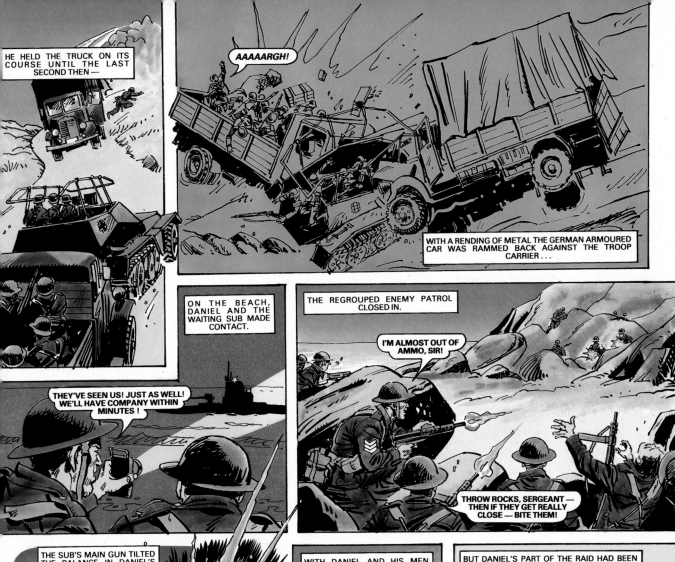

HE HELD THE TRUCK ON ITS COURSE UNTIL THE LAST SECOND THEN —

AAAAARGH!

WITH A RENDING OF METAL THE GERMAN ARMOURED CAR WAS RAMMED BACK AGAINST THE TROOP CARRIER . . .

ON THE BEACH, DANIEL AND THE WAITING SUB MADE CONTACT.

THEY'VE SEEN US! JUST AS WELL! WE'LL HAVE COMPANY WITHIN MINUTES !

THE REGROUPED ENEMY PATROL CLOSED IN.

I'M ALMOST OUT OF AMMO, SIR!

THROW ROCKS, SERGEANT — THEN IF THEY GET REALLY CLOSE — BITE THEM!

THE SUB'S MAIN GUN TILTED THE BALANCE IN DANIEL'S FAVOUR.

WELL DONE, THE NAVY!

WITH DANIEL AND HIS MEN SAFELY ABOARD, THE SUB HEADED FOR HOME.

WE LOST THREE, SIR. MORGAN'S PRETTY BAD, BUT HE SHOULD MAKE IT. YOU DID US PROUD, SIR.

I ACTUALLY ENJOYED IT! WONDER HOW TOBY FARED!

BUT DANIEL'S PART OF THE RAID HAD BEEN THE SOLE SUCCESS. BACK AT BASE AT THE DEBRIEFING —

JOHNSON'S GROUP NEVER REACHED THE RADAR STATION. THEY WERE BEATEN BACK WITH HEAVY CASUALTIES.

TOBY CARSTAIRS' GROUP DIDN'T MAKE IT BACK TO THEIR RENDEZVOUS POINT. ALL ARE POSTED MISSING.

TOBY HADN'T BEEN A REAL FRIEND, MORE A FELLOW CONSPIRATOR, BUT FOR ONCE DANIEL FELT ON HIS OWN.

BY THE WAY, CONWAY, YOU'VE BEEN GRANTED A WEEKEND PASS. YOU'RE TO REPORT HOME IMMEDIATELY. KEEP YOUR PART IN OUR OPERATIONS TO YOURSELF.

I WON'T SAY A WORD.

LET'S AGREE TO KEEP OUT OF EACH OTHER'S LIVES.

OH, IF ONLY THAT WERE POSSIBLE.

PUZZLED BY THE SUMMONS HOME, DANIEL FOUND HIS FATHER AWAITING HIM ANGRILY.

DON'T PRETEND YOU DON'T KNOW ABOUT THE COURT-MARTIAL OF SECOND LIEUTENANT GORDON FOLKS! AN OFFICER WHO STOLE MONEY TO PAY GAMBLING DEBTS — TO YOU!

AM I TO FACE ANY CHARGES, FATHER?

DANIEL WAS HALF-AWARE OF HIS MOTHER WATCHING BUT STIFF-NECKED PRIDE STOPPED HIM FROM LOOKING BACK.

CHARLES, HE'S YOUR SON!

I HAVE NO SON, ELIZABETH! AND NEITHER HAVE YOU!

THE EXCITEMENT OF THE RAID HAD PUSHED THE GAMBLING INCIDENT TO THE BACK OF DANIEL'S MIND BUT IT SEEMED THE PAST WAS CATCHING UP WITH HIM.

NO, YOU'RE NOT! THIS IS THE LAST TIME I BAIL YOU OUT OF TROUBLE, BOY. YOU'RE A DISGRACE TO THE NAME OF CONWAY!

SO YOU KEEP REMINDING ME, FATHER.

MAY, 1944 — AT ONE OF A THOUSAND BRIEFINGS —

CONWAY AND FOSTER WILL STRIKE SOUTH AND TAKE THE TARGET BRIDGE. IT IS VITAL THAT THIS BRIDGE REMAINS INTACT UNTIL OUR ARMOUR ARRIVES.

DANIEL WAS IN THE BIG LEAGUE NOW AND HIS WAS A TOUGH TARGET.

IF WE CAN GET OUR ARMOUR ACROSS THE BRIDGE, WE CAN ADVANCE INLAND. IF THE BRIDGE IS BLOWN, IT'LL DELAY THE BREAKOUT FROM THE BEACHES.

DANIEL FOUND HIMSELF TINGLING WITH EXCITEMENT.

HOW LONG SHALL WE BE REQUIRED TO HOLD THE BRIDGE, SIR?

A MAXIMUM OF TWELVE HOURS — A LONG DAY, DANIEL.

REHEARSAL FOLLOWED REHEARSAL UNTIL ON JUNE 5TH, 1944, DANIEL AND HIS MEN BOARDED THEIR GLIDERS — DESTINATION NORMANDY!

HAVE YOU HEARD FROM THAT OLD MAN OF YOURS LATELY, DANIEL?

WHAT OLD MAN?

DANIEL HAD RECEIVED NO WORD FROM HIS FATHER FOR MORE THAN A YEAR AND HIS LETTERS TO HIS MOTHER HAD GONE UNANSWERED.

THIS BUSINESS OF BEING BANISHED FROM THE FAMILY IS EATING YOU UP INSIDE.

YOU'RE TALKING OUT OF THE BACK OF YOUR NECK, JOHNNY.

DANIEL COULD STAND HIS FATHER CUTTING HIM OFF BUT NO WORD FROM HIS MOTHER HURT HIM MORE THAN HE CARED TO ADMIT.

A SMOOTH FLIGHT ACROSS THE CHANNEL ENDED WHEN FLAK GREETED THEM SOON AFTER CROSSING THE NORMANDY COAST.

STAND-BY! CAST-OFF ZONE! LINK ARMS AND FEET UP! BRACE YOURSELVES!

GLIDER LANDINGS WERE TRICKY AT BEST AND THE LANDING GROUND HAD FEW OBSTACLES — BUT ENOUGH TO CAUSE DAMAGE TO SOME GLIDERS.

DANIEL'S TROOPS HAD NO MAJOR CASUALTIES.

ALL RIGHT, MOVE IT, LADS!

THEY FOUND THE ROAD AND MOVED SOUTH TOWARDS MYERVILLE.

THAT'S OUR MAN UP AHEAD. WHAT'S HE WANT?

BUT THE ADVANCE SCOUT DIDN'T HAVE A CHANCE TO REPORT AS THE ENEMY SUDDENLY OPENED FIRE.

A PILL-BOX! THAT WASN'T ON THE INTELLIGENCE BRIEF EITHER.

THE GROUP WERE PINNED DOWN.

KEEP 'EM OCCUPIED, JOHNNY! SERGEANT TOWNS, BRING TWO MEN AND FOLLOW ME!

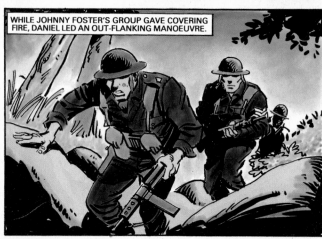

WHILE JOHNNY FOSTER'S GROUP GAVE COVERING FIRE, DANIEL LED AN OUT-FLANKING MANOEUVRE.

DANIEL'S WORST FEARS WERE CONFIRMED AS THE OUTLINES OF TWO CONCRETE PILL-BOXES LOOMED OUT OF THE DARKNESS.

THEY'LL TAKE SOME SHIFTING, SERGEANT. WE'LL USE GRENADES!

DANIEL BEGAN HIS ZIG-ZAG RUN ACROSS THE FIELD . . .

DON'T JUST WATCH HIM! GIVE HIM COVERING FIRE.

. . . THEN POSTED A GRENADE.

FROM ME TO YOU WITH LOVE, FRITZ!

THE SECOND PILL-BOX SUFFERED THE SAME FATE.

MOVE ON! WE'VE GOT TO KEEP MOVING!

TOPPING THE HILL DANIEL SIGHTED THE OBJECTIVE.

I'M ALL FOR SETTING AN EXAMPLE, DANIEL, BUT WHAT YOU DID BACK THERE WAS CRAZY! WHAT ARE YOU TRYING TO PROVE?

DON'T KNOW WHAT YOU'RE TALKING ABOUT, JOHNNY.

JOHNNY FOSTER LED HIS GROUP AGAINST THE VILLAGE OF MYERVILLE, WHILE DANIEL'S HEADED FOR THE BRIDGE. THEY WERE SOON UNDER HEAVY FIRE.

THEN DANIEL FOUND HIMSELF FACED BY THE WORST POSSIBLE ENEMY OPPOSITION.

TIGER TANK! RIGHT ACROSS THE APPROACH, SIR!

WE'VE NOTHING HEAVY ENOUGH TO SHIFT THAT MONSTER!

DANIEL DEPLOYED HIS MEN AROUND THE BRIDGE APPROACH BUT EACH MOVEMENT BROUGHT ANSWERING FIRE.

THE ONLY WAY WE'LL KNOCK IT OUT IS A COUPLE OF GRENADES DOWN THE HATCH!

WE HAVEN'T A HOPE OF GETTING THAT CLOSE. CAN'T WE CALL UP AN AIR STRIKE?

NO CHANCE, SERGEANT. THEY COULD MISS THE TANK AND BLOW THE BRIDGE — WHICH RATHER DEFEATS THE OBJECT OF OUR OPERATION.

DAWN — AND JOHNNY FOSTER'S MEN HAD TAKEN THE VILLAGE.

GOOD NEWS, DANIEL! WE CAPTURED JERRIES' STORES IN THE VILLAGE AND AMONG THEM WAS A PORTABLE FLAME-THROWER.

GOOD NEWS — YES, BUT THE BAD NEWS IS IT'S A CLOSE-RANGE WEAPON.

DANIEL'S PLAN WAS BASIC AND DEPENDED ON LUCK, A COMMODITY HE FELT HE ALWAYS HAD WITH HIM.

SO FAR, SO GOOD. KEEP HIS ATTENTION, JOHNNY!

ALTHOUGH HE KNEW THE FLAME-THROWER HAD A RANGE OF SIXTY YARDS, DANIEL WENT IN CLOSE FOR A CERTAIN KILL.

THE BLAZING TIGER BACKED ACROSS THE BRIDGE.

DANIEL PRESSED HOME THE ATTACK.

THERE SHE GOES, LADS! COME ON!

YOU DID IT, OLD BOY! HE'S HAD ENOUGH!

BUT DANIEL HAD STRETCHED HIS LUCK TOO FAR. WITHERING ENEMY MACHINE-GUN FIRE STOPPED HIM IN HIS TRACKS.

AAARGH!

JOHNNY FOSTER DRAGGED DANIEL BACK.

IT'S NO USE, DANIEL! WE'RE STILL PINNED DOWN.

MEANWHILE, AT THE BEACH-HEAD, DANIEL'S FATHER AND HIS UNIT WERE IMPATIENT AT THE DELAY INLAND, UNAWARE THAT DANIEL WAS INVOLVED.

MYERVILLE HAS BEEN TAKEN BUT JERRY IS STILL HOLDING THE BRIDGE.

CONFOUND THE DELAY! I'M GOING ON FOR A PERSONAL RECCE.

SHEER WILL-POWER GAVE DANIEL STRENGTH, AS HE SLASHED AT THE FUSE-WIRE WITH HIS BAYONET. BUT EVEN THEN HE WAS CAUGHT BY A HAIL OF FIRE.

CAN'T CUT THE FUSES — CHARGES WILL GO OFF SOON.

THEN WITH A LAST LOOK BACK AT HIS FATHER, DANIEL STEPPED INTO OBLIVION.

ONLY ONE WAY LEFT . . .

DANIEL!

LEAVING THE STRICKEN COLONEL BEHIND, JOHNNY FOSTER LED A CHARGE ACROSS THE BRIDGE.

AT THEM, MEN!

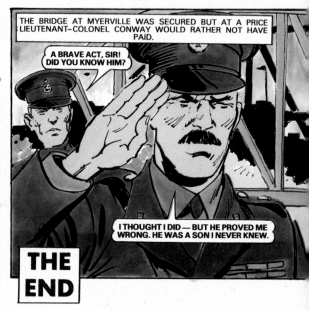

THE BRIDGE AT MYERVILLE WAS SECURED BUT AT A PRICE LIEUTENANT–COLONEL CONWAY WOULD RATHER NOT HAVE PAID.

A BRAVE ACT, SIR! DID YOU KNOW HIM?

I THOUGHT I DID — BUT HE PROVED ME WRONG. HE WAS A SON I NEVER KNEW.

THE END

IN MARCH, 1944, A SMALL CONVOY OF BRITISH FOURTEENTH ARMY SUPPLY TROOPS WAS TRAVELLING ALONG THE HIGHWAY FROM DINAPUR IN INDIA TO THE RIVER CHINDIVIN IN BURMA. IN THE LEAD VEHICLE WERE LIEUTENANT JAMES AND LANCE CORPORAL "JUNGLI" WOOD OF THE R.A.S.C.

LOOK OUT!

WHERE DID *HE* COME FROM?

MILESTONE 95.
IMPHAL →

ROAD CUT — JAPS EVERYWHERE! WIPED OUT FREDDIE COLUMN... WOUNDED GETTING AWAY... AHH...

SIR — HE'S DEAD!

WHY SO SURPRISED, WOOD? YOU MUST HAVE SEEN DEAD MEN IN YOUR TIME WITH THE CHINDIT MULE COLUMN.

THEN THE MORTAR BARRAGE HIT THEM —

ALBERT TONKS WAS NEW TO BURMA AND JUNGLI WAS HIS IDEA OF A HERO.

JAP MORTARS! GET UNDER COVER!

IT AIN'T FAIR THE WAY JAMES GETS ON AT YOU, JUNGLI. HE'S JEALOUS BECAUSE YOU WENT BEHIND THE JAP LINES WITH THE CHINDITS.

A BASE WALLAH LIKE HIM CAN'T REALISE THE HORROR OF BEING A GUERILLA FIGHTER LIKE US CHINDITS.

JUNGLI, DO YOU RECKON WE SHOULD CHARGE LIKE WHEN YOU WAS AMBUSHED WITH THE MULE COLUMN?

HUH — ER, BETTER WEIGH UP THE SITUATION FIRST, ALBERT.

THE LIEUTENANT'S ALIVE. WE'D BETTER GET HIM INTO COVER.

WOOD, I TRUST YOU AREN'T THINKING OF PULLING ME TO SAFETY UNDER A TRUCK LOADED WITH AMMUNITION. AN OLD CHINDIT LIKE YOU SHOULD KNOW WE HAVE TO BREAK OUT OF THIS AMBUSH.

WHAT — ER, DEAD RIGHT, SIR.

MOUNT UP, YOU LOT! WE'RE GETTING OUT OF HERE.

LEAVING BEHIND A BURNING TRUCK, THE COLUMN MOVED OUT UNDER MORTAR AND SMALL-ARMS FIRE.

NOT MUCH BLOOD, SIR.

THANK YOU, DRIVER TONKS — NOW LISTEN. THIS WAY WE ARE HEADING INTO JAPS ACCORDING TO THAT DEAD DESPATCH RIDER.

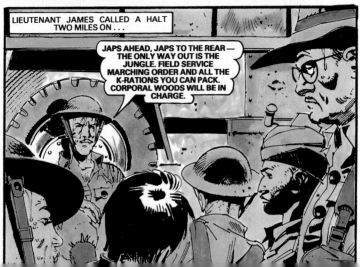

LIEUTENANT JAMES CALLED A HALT TWO MILES ON . . .

JAPS AHEAD, JAPS TO THE REAR — THE ONLY WAY OUT IS THE JUNGLE. FIELD SERVICE MARCHING ORDER AND ALL THE K-RATIONS YOU CAN PACK. CORPORAL WOODS WILL BE IN CHARGE.

AS THE MEN PREPARED TO MARCH —

SIR, THERE'S SOMETHING I OUGHT TO TELL YOU.

LIKE YOU NEVER SAW ANY CHINDIT ACTION? WOOD, I'VE SEEN YOUR RECORD. YOU DID HAVE JUNGLE TRAINING THOUGH AND I'M COUNTING ON YOU TO SAVE THESE MEN.

WE COULD STILL RIG A STRETCHER FOR YOU, SIR.

I'LL BE DEAD INSIDE A MILE IF YOU TRY MOVING ME, WOOD.

THE TRUCKS WERE BOOBY-TRAPPED.

ALBERT, MAKE SURE THE GRENADE DETONATOR SLEEVE AIN'T BLOCKED. JUST A BIT OF GREASE OR DIRT AND YOU CAN GET A PREMATURE EXPLOSION WHEN YOU SCREW HOME THE BASE PLUG.

SO HELP ME IF I EVER SAW SUCH AN HORRIBLE SHOWER. ONE LOOK AT YOU AND THE JAPS'LL DIE LAUGHING.

A WINDBAG LEADING A BUNCH OF LOW GRADE BASE TROOPS! I HOPE THEY MAKE IT, BUT I HAVE MY DOUBTS.

LATER —

JAPONI COME!

INGRIZ, BETTER DIE THAN SHAME OF BEING PRISONER.

MY OWN FEELINGS EXACTLY, SPORT. SHALL WE BEGIN THE DYING?

95

LOOK! THE JAPS ARE COMING AFTER US.

JUNGLI'S PARTY MOVED OUT — FAST!

ARE YOU THINKING THIS IS JUST THE SPOT FOR AN AMBUSH LIKE YOU AND MAD JACK PULLED OFF WHEN THAT JAP PATROL CHASED YOU, JUNGLI?

WHAT? OH, YES. HUM!

THIS BUNCH IS EXHAUSTED ALREADY.

IF WE HIT THE NIPS HARD, WE BUY A CHANCE TO GET AWAY — HEY! WHERE ARE YOU GOING?

CORPORAL, YOU WANT TO BE FIGHTING JAPANESE — GOOD. YOU BE FIGHTING THEM BUT WE BE GOING ON.

WRONG! YOU STAY AND FIGHT — OR GET SHOT. RIGHT, CORPORAL?

HUH? ER, DEAD RIGHT, ALBERT.

JUNGLI PLACED HIS AMBUSH —

KEEP YOUR HEAD DOWN — STAY STILL. NO FIRING TILL THE GRENADES GO OFF.

SAHIB, THE BOLT IRON KEEPS COMING AWAY IN MY HAND.

ASLAM, MAYBE YOU'D BE SAFER HITTING THE JAPS WITH THAT RIFLE.

THE FIRST GRENADES WENT OFF—

ALBERT — FIRE!

CONTINUED ON PAGE 114.

Commando

H.M.S. WHASKERBY WAS A SHIP OF WAR BUT NO FIGHTING SHIP. WHAT ELSE COULD YOU EXPECT FROM A SHIP WHOSE CREW HAD MUTINIED? THEN CAME THE DAY SHE LOST HER TITLE —

SHIP OF SHAME

SPRING, 1944 — THE ENGLISH CHANNEL. A FLOTILLA OF GERMAN TORPEDO BOATS INCHES INTO POSITION FOR AN ATTACK ON A BRITISH COASTAL CONVOY OF TANK LANDING CRAFT ON A NIGHT EXERCISE.

SUB-LIEUTENANT BILL BRODIE SPOTTED THE ATTACKERS.

E-BOATS! HARD A STARBOARD! OPEN UP, GUNNERS!

THOUGHT YOU'D TAKE US BY SURPRISE, FRITZ? WRONG!

LEADING SEAMAN JACK DESTRY'S OERLIKON WAS SOON IN ACTION.

WILL ANYONE HEAR OUR ATTACK REPORT?

AGAINST THE LOW-LYING FAST MOVING RAIDERS THE LANDING SHIPS WERE HELPLESS.

THEY'RE LIKE FOXES AMONGST CHICKENS!

98

AAAAAH!

SUDDENLY HELP CAME OUT OF THE DARKNESS —

THE NAVY'S HERE! COME ON, LADS!

IN A SECOND THE TABLES WERE TURNED —

ANOTHER DESTROYER APPEARED —

MUST BE A FLOTILLA! THEM E-BOATS AIN'T HANGING AROUND TO FIND OUT ANYHOW!

YOU OKAY, SIR? SOME DESTROYERS HAVE SHOWN OFF THE E-BOATS! TWO OF OUR LOT HAVE BEEN SUNK.

THANKS, DESTRY. RIGHT ARM'S A BIT FUNNY, BUT LET'S SEE ABOUT FINDING SURVIVORS.

ALTHOUGH IN PAIN, BRODIE SUPERVISED THE PICKING UP OF SURVIVORS —

EASY WITH HIM!

THE SKIPPER'S A RIGHT BRICK.

BILL HAD A BROKEN ARM AND SHRAPNEL WOUNDS TO HIS CHEST AND SHOULDER —

YOU'LL BE HERE FOR SOME TIME. WAR COULD BE OVER BY THE TIME YOU GET OUT.

TIME PASSED — NOVEMBER, 1944. TWO YOUNG SAILORS, JOHNNY STAFFORD AND "GINGER" HAGGERTY, SPECULATED ON THEIR FIRST POSTING —

I'LL BE GLAD TO GET ON TO A PROPER SHIP.

WONDER WHAT SHE'LL BE . . . CRUISER, CORVETTE?

ABLE SEAMAN MICK SHANKS, A HOARY REGULAR WITH SERVICE IN THE PEACETIME NAVY, SNEERED AT THEM —

YOU HOSTILITY-ONLY BLOKES DON'T KNOW WHEN YOU'RE WELL OFF. JUST WAIT TILL YOU'RE IN A FORCE TEN GALE.

AW, LAY OFF, SHANKS! THEY'RE JUST KIDS.

YOUR DRAFT CHITTIES TO JOIN H.M.S. WHASKERBY IN SUNNY LIVERPOOL. AND THE BEST OF BRITISH LUCK!

SHANKS MOANED ALL THE WAY —

WHOEVER HEARD OF THE WHASKERBY? I SHOULDN'T BE GOIN' BACK TO SEA. I'VE BEEN TORPEDOED TWICE.

MORE LIKELY YOU FELL IN, SHANKSY!

IT WAS LATE WHEN THEY ARRIVED AT LIVERPOOL — AND RECEIVED THIS FIRST LOOK AT THEIR NEW POSTING.

THAT'S THE WHASKERBY! WOT'S IT SUPPOSED TO BE, SHANKS?

THAT'S AN L.S.I. (L.), GINGER . . . A LANDING SHIP INFANTRY — LARGE! CONVERTED LIBERTY SHIP.

GEE, I EXPECTED BETTER'N THIS, JOHNNY . . . A CORVETTE AT LEAST.

YEH, WHAT A LOUSY BREAK!

DOWN ON THE MESS DECK —

THE BLOOMIN' BLACK HOLE OF CALCUTTA!

REMINDS ME OF THE KOP ON A SAT'DAY AFTERNOON!

I'LL SLING ME HAMMOCK HERE.

NO, YOU WON'T! THAT'S MY PLACE.

JOHNNY WAS TOLD TO SLEEP ON A TABLE, GINGER ON A LOCKER —

YOU TELL 'IM, HOOKIE! SLAP THEM YOUNGSTERS DOWN.

I'M DESTRY — THE NEW LEADING RATING IN THIS MESS. THE ACCOMMODATION'S BAD. YOU COULD DO WORSE, BUT NOT A LOT.

NEXT DAY, THE NEW FIRST LIEUTENANT, BILL BRODIE, RECOVERED FROM HIS WOUNDS, REPORTED TO LIEUTENANT COMMANDER HOWE.

ABOUT TIME, TOO. THIS SHIP IS GOING TO POT.

I'M A STICKLER FOR DISCIPLINE AND I'LL COME DOWN HARD ON ANY SLACKNESS, YOU HEAR? KEEP THE MEN ON THEIR TOES.

BILL BRODIE HAD COME UP THROUGH THE RANKS. HE WASN'T LONG IN ASSESSING THE CREW —

RUM LOT, THIS . . . SCRAPINGS OF THE SHORE BASES, GASH BODS, YOUNG RATINGS WHO'VE NEVER BEEN TO SEA. MUST'VE BEEN ASSEMBLED IN A HURRY.

SHANKS WAS THE FIRST SLACKER TO FALL FOUL OF BRODIE.

YOU . . . STOP SWINGING THE LEAD. I'VE GOT MY EYE ON YOU!

AYE-AYE, SIR! JUST TAKIN' A BREATHER.

LATER —

RIGHT PIG THAT NUMBER ONE. CAME UP THROUGH THE HAWSE-PIPE — THEM KIND KNOW ALL THE DODGES!

RECKON YOU DON'T LIKE BEING IN THE NAVY, SHANKS. I'M SURPRISED YOU JOINED.

I DON'T LIKE THIS TUB, THAT'S FOR SURE!

BLOOMIN' GRIPER . . . ONE IN EVERY MESS. YOU KIDS DON'T LISTEN TO HIM. JUST KEEP YOUR OWN YARD-ARMS CLEAR AN' YOU'LL BE OKAY.

TROUBLES AROSE WHEN THE SHIP BEGAN HER TRIALS —

YOU BLITHERING IDIOT, COX'N. YOU'VE HIT THE JETTY!

SORRY, SIR! SHE'S SLOW TO ANSWER THE HELM.

SHOOTING PRACTICE WASN'T MUCH BETTER —

DISGRACEFUL, NUMBER ONE! ALMOST HIT THE TOW SHIP! LAY ON EXTRA GUN DRILLS.

EVENTUALLY WHASKERBY SAILED AND HER DESTINATION WAS DISCLOSED —

WE ARE TO JOIN THE U.S. PACIFIC CAMPAIGN TO ASSIST IN LANDING TROOPS AND ACT AS A HEADQUARTERS SHIP.

THE PACIFIC! PINEAPPLES — BANANAS! GREAT!

WHY CAN'T THE YANKS FINISH THEIR OWN WAR? WE'VE DONE OUR STINT THIS SIDE.

BELLYACHIN' AGAIN, SHANKS? AT LEAST WE'LL GET SOME SUNSHINE WHERE WE'RE GOIN'.

THEY JOINED A CONVOY OFF NORTHERN IRELAND AND SET COURSE ACROSS THE GREY, HEAVING ATLANTIC —

KEEP YOUR EYES PEELED FOR CONDORS, — LONG RANGE RECONNAISSANCE AIRCRAFT. THEY SUMMON UP THE U-BOATS.

AYE-AYE, SIR!

MORE THAN ONE SEAMAN WAS SEASICK AS THE WHASKERBY PLUNGED AND REELED IN HEAVY SEAS.

OOOH . . . I WISH I'D JOINED THE R.A.F., JOHNNY.

MAYBE YOU'D BEEN AIR-SICK THEN, GINGER.

JOHNNY TOO HAD HIS PRIVATE WORRIES —

IT'S SO CROWDED! WE'D NEVER GET OUT OF HERE IF HIT BY A TORPEDO.

THE WHASKERBY HAD DIFFICULTY KEEPING UP, AS SHE BELCHED SMOKE, THE CURSE OF ALL CONVOYS —

EVERY SUB FOR MILES AROUND WILL BE QUEUING UP FOR A GO AT US! TELL 'EM TO STOP THAT SMOKE!

HOPELESS SHOOTING, BRODIE! NOWHERE NEAR!

THEY'D ONLY A GLIMPSE OF THE TARGET, SIR!

FOR TWO DAYS AND NIGHTS THE ATTACKS CONTINUED AS THE OVERWORKED ESCORTS SOUGHT OUT THE UNSEEN ATTACKERS WITH UNSEEN RESULTS.

LET'S HOPE THEY HAVE SOME LUCK, GINGER!

THEN AT LAST THE ATTACKS CEASED. IN FRIENDLIER WATERS, THE LANDING SHIP SPLIT FROM THE REST OF THE CONVOY AND HEADED SOUTH TO THE PANAMA CANAL AND ON INTO THE PACIFIC. BUT WHASKERBY'S TROUBLES WEREN'T OVER. WHEN SHE BERTHED AT A TROPICAL ISLAND, THE MEN WERE WORKED NON-STOP IN THEIR HEAVY OVERALLS IN THE BROILING HEAT —

THE MESS DECKS WERE AIRLESS AND INFESTED WITH COCK-ROACHES AND RATS —

PUT YOUR BACKS INTO IT! THIS ISN'T A PICNIC YOU'RE ON!

IT'S ALL RIGHT FOR THEM PIGS IN THEIR WHITE SHIRTS AND SHORTS. WE SHOULD BE IN TROPICAL GEAR.

WAAAAH, WHAT'S THAT?

IT'S A RAT, SHANKS! THE BIGGEST I EVER SAW!

AAAAAOOOOOOOOH!

BLIMEY, SHANKS! I THINK THE RAT WAS MORE SCARED THAN YOU.

DRINKING WATER WAS RATIONED AND THE FOOD WAS DREADFUL —

THESE BISCUITS HAVE WEEVILS IN THEM!

MEANTIME, LIEUTENANT COMMANDER HOWE HAD BEEN INVITED TO DINE WITH THE OFFICERS IN THEIR WARDROOM. A POOR LOT, THEY DIDN'T SEEM TO CARE HOW THE RATINGS FARED —

I BELIEVE IN A BIT OF TRADITIONAL CEREMONY. DON'T SUPPOSE THAT'LL BE YOUR STYLE, NUMBER ONE, COMING UP THROUGH THE RANKS AND THAT. "PIGSTY", THEY CALL THE WARDROOM, DON'T THEY?

WE'LL HAVE TROUBLE ON THE LOWER DECK, UNLESS WE EASE UP ON 'EM AND HAVE THE YANKS SUPPLY BETTER FOOD.

YOU'RE AN ALARMIST, BRODIE. IF ANYTHING, DISCIPLINE SHOULD BE INCREASED. THIS IS THE SLACKEST CREW I'VE EVER SAILED WITH.

ABSOLUTELY, SIR!

NEXT DAY, AS THE WHASKERBY LAY IN A PACIFIC ISLAND BASE TO TAKE ON AUSTRALIAN TROOPS —

MUCK! UNEATABLE MUCK!

PICK THAT UP, SAILOR! THE REST OF YOU GET ON DECK AT THE DOUBLE!

YOU PICK IT UP! WE'RE STAYIN' RIGHT HERE!

THE MIDSHIPMAN FLED TO BE REPLACED BY BILL BRODIE —

DON'T BE SO STUPID! ON DECK AT ONCE AND WE'LL FORGET THIS!

YOU CAN GET LOST AS WELL!

OKAY, YOU'VE GOT FIVE MINUTES . . . THEN BE UP ON DECK. I'LL SEE YOUR GRIEVANCES ARE HEARD.

BUT BRODIE'S REQUEST TO THE CAPTAIN FELL ON DEAF EARS. MEANWHILE, THE CREW PASSED TWO HOURS IN HEATED ARGUMENT.

BRODIE'S A GOOD MAN. I SAILED WITH HIM IN LANDING CRAFT. HE'LL SEE US OKAY. LET'S GET UP THERE.

HE'S STILL AN OFFICER. I DON'T TRUST 'EM.

EVENTUALLY DESTRY WON THE ARGUMENT —

SIR. I BEG TO SPEAK . . . OUR FOOD . . .

DISPERSE AT ONCE AND PREPARE FOR SEA. THIS IS MUTINY.

GET LOST! WE WANT SATISFACTION. WE AIN'T SAILIN' TILL WE GET IT!

TURN OUT THE MARINES, LIEUTENANT.

AN APPEAL FOR HELP BROUGHT AUSTRALIAN TROOPS WHO HAD BEEN WAITING TO EMBARK AND ORDER WAS RESTORED.

YOU LOT ARE FOR BEHIND BARS!

CAN'T BE ANY WORSE THAN THIS TUB!

WHILE BILL BRODIE WAS CONFINED TO HIS CABIN, DESTRY WAS PARADED BEFORE THE CAPTAIN.

I WILL NOT TOLERATE OFFICERS OR LEADING HANDS WHO OBSTRUCT ME. I REGARD IT AS MUTINY.

BUT I TRIED TO STOP IT!

THE MUTINEERS SHOULD HAVE BEEN LEFT ASHORE IN A MILITARY PRISON BUT THE SHIP HAD TO SAIL IMMEDIATELY AND NO REPLACEMENTS WERE AVAILABLE. AS SHE LEFT HARBOUR—

THAT THE SHIP OF SHAME REFUSED TO SAIL?

YEH, COWARDLY LIMEYS DIDN'T WANNA FIGHT. SHOULDA SHOT THE LOT.

JOHNNY STAFFORD AND GINGER HAGGERTY REALISED HOW LUCKY THEY WERE NOT TO HAVE BEEN INVOLVED IN THE FIGHT.

IT AIN'T RIGHT, LOCKING DESTRY UP WITH SHANKS AND THE OTHERS, GINGER. HE TRIED TO STOP THE MUTINY.

BESET BY OLD TROUBLES, THE WHASKERBY JUDDERED AND GROANED THROUGH THE HEAVY SEAS.

WE SOUND LIKE A SHIP LOAD OF PIGS . . .

THE TASK FORCE THINK WE SMELL LIKE ONE. THEY THINK WE'RE YELLOW.

YELLOW OR NOT, THE WHASKERBY LANDED HER AUSSIE TROOPS ON TIME ON THEIR TARGET BEACH . . .

GOOD LUCK, DIGGER!

WITH THE COOK YOU'VE GOT, YOU NEED THE LUCK, MATES.

. . . HOWEVER, THE LONG VOYAGES OVER THE ATLANTIC THEN THE PACIFIC HAD TAKEN THEIR TOLL.

THIS SHIP WILL RETURN TO BASE FOR A MAJOR REFIT. YOU AND YOUR FELLOW MUTINEERS WILL FACE CHARGES THERE, BRODIE.

TWO DAYS LATER, AS IF TO PROLONG THE VOYAGE OF SHAME, A THICK FOG SLOWED THE WHASKERBY DOWN EVEN FURTHER.

OUR RADAR HAS PACKED UP AND WE NEED EVERY HAND TO ACT AS LOOKOUTS. RELEASE THE MUTINEERS AND POST THEM.

AYE, AYE, SIR!

WE'RE BEING SHELLED! BUT WHO'S DOING IT?

WHO CARES? THEY'VE GOT RADAR — WE DON'T!

THE WHASKERBY SHUDDERED AS A SECOND SALVO STRUCK HER.

AAAAANGH!

THE COX'N IS HIT!

AS THE SHIP REELED TO THE HAMMER BLOWS OF THE INCOMING SHELLS, HOWE PANICKED—

WE CAN'T SEE TO FIGHT BACK. SAVE THE CREW! ABANDON SHIP!

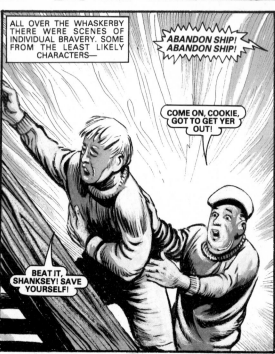

ALL OVER THE WHASKERBY THERE WERE SCENES OF INDIVIDUAL BRAVERY. SOME FROM THE LEAST LIKELY CHARACTERS—

ABANDON SHIP! ABANDON SHIP!

COME ON, COOKIE, GOT TO GET YER OUT!

BEAT IT, SHANKSEY! SAVE YOURSELF!

BILL DECIDED TO RETAKE THE WHASKERBY.

KEEP IT QUIET DOWN THERE!

JAPS! LET'S GET 'EM WHILE THEY'RE FIGHTING THE FIRE!

GET IN CLOSE SO THEY CAN'T USE THOSE RIFLES!

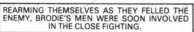

REARMING THEMSELVES AS THEY FELLED THE ENEMY, BRODIE'S MEN WERE SOON INVOLVED IN THE CLOSE FIGHTING.

BEHIND YOU, SIR!

THANKS, DESTRY!

NO SWEAT, SIR!

A FEW MINUTES LATER IT WAS ALL OVER, THE JAPS NO MATCH FOR THE DOUGHTY SAILORS —

THAT WAS SOME SCRAP!

NAH, WE HAD A TOUGHER TIME AGAINST OUR OWN MARINES!

JAP CRUISER TO STARBOARD!

THE TOYOKAWA SENSHA!

NO RADIO TO SEND FOR HELP — NO GUN TO FIGHT WITH! BRODIE TICKED THE PROBLEMS OFF MENTALLY THEN CAME TO HIS DECISION!

ATTACK? BUT HOW, SIR?

WE'LL RAM THEM. WE'VE NO CHOICE. THEY'D SINK US IF WE TRIED TO RUN!

111

FULL ASTERN! WE'RE KEEPING HER AFLOAT!

AS THE WHASKERBY FOUGHT CLEAR, THE SEA RUSHED INTO THE GAPING HOLE IN THE JAP CRUISER'S SIDE.

KEEP GOING!

THEY'RE FIGHTING TO THE END — BUT THEY *ARE* GOING DOWN. NOW LET'S SEE IF WE CAN SURVIVE OURSELVES.

AT DAWN AN AMERICAN DESTROYER APPEARED AND TOOK THEM IN TOW. A DAY OR TWO LATER THEY JOINED THE REST OF THE FLEET—

WE AIN'T NO SHIP OF SHAME NOW, EH?

THERE WAS STILL NO NEWS OF HOWE AND THE OTHER OFFICERS WHEN THE ADMIRAL CAME ABOARD—

A BRAVE ACTION, BRODIE. AND IN VIEW OF IT THERE WILL BE NO CHARGES AGAINST YOU OR YOUR MEN.

A FURTHER INVESTIGATION REVEALED THE TRUTH ABOUT HOWE AND HIS OFFICERS WHO HAD BEEN FOUND ADRIFT IN THE BOAT. BILL BRODIE WAS GIVEN COMMAND OF THE WHASKERBY BEFORE HEADING FOR AUSTRALIA AND A REFIT.

GREAT PLACE, AUSTRALIA. EVEN SHANKSEY WOULD'VE LIKED IT.

I WOULDN'T COUNT ON THAT. I'LL BET HE'D COMPLAIN ABOUT THE HEAT, THE BEACHES, THE FOOD . . .

THE END

MAKE SMOKE!

A lead escort vessel lays a smoke screen as its sister ship prepares to engage approaching enemy raiders.

DEATH MARCH TO KOHIMA
CONTINUED FROM PAGE 96.

THE JAP SERGEANT ESCAPED THE AMBUSH—

BANZAI!

STEN'S JAMMED!

HELP REACHED JUNGLI—

EXCUSE PLEASE, SAHIB!

RIFLE GOOD FOR HITTING JAPONI LIKE YOU ARE SAYING, SAHIB.

ER... YES... QUITE SO...

WE'D BETTER CAMP BEFORE DARK. CAN'T RISK A FIRE AND GUARDS WILL HAVE TO BE POSTED.

RIGHT, JUNGLI!

WE ARE KILLING THEM ALL. BY JOVE, WE GIVING DASHED GOOD SCRAP, EH?

WE DIDN'T DO SO BADLY. NOW LET'S GET GOING.

THE NIGHT PASSED QUIETLY ENOUGH . . .

... BUT DAWN BROUGHT PANIC.

STAND-TO!

A SHOT! WHAT'S HAPPENED?

THE HEADS OF THOSE NIPS WE TANGLED WITH YESTERDAY!

SOMEBODY IS PUTTING THEM THERE, SAHIB. SOMEBODY VERY QUIET. GUARDS ARE HEARING NOTHING.

ALBERT, UNWRAP A COUPLE OF K-RATION CHOC BARS AND WAVE 'EM IN THE AIR.

ALBERT'S WAVING OF CANDY CAUSED A STIRRING AT THE EDGE OF THE JUNGLE.

NAGA TRIBESMEN! THEY USED TO BE HEADHUNTERS AND BRINGING US THOSE HEADS MUST BE A SIGN OF RESPECT.

JUNGLI EXCHANGED SIGNS WITH THE TRIBESMEN.

I THINK THEY UNDERSTAND THERE WILL BE MORE CHOC BARS IF THEY TAKE US TO THE NEAREST BRITISH UNIT.

GUIDED BY THE NAGAS THE GROUP MOVED ON, BUT THAT AFTERNOON —

THE ROAD — AND LOOK! SOME OF OUR BLOKES MOVING UP.

NO, ALBERT. NOT OUR BLOKES.

JAPS IN CAPTURED BRITISH TRUCKS.

SAHIB, I AM WATCHING OVER YOU. SEE HOW I AM FINDING HOW TO PUT THE AWKWARD BIT OF IRON IN MY BUNDOOK.

ASLAM, KEEP YOUR FINGER AWAY FROM THE TRIGGER.

BUT ASLAM WASN'T GOOD AT TAKING ADVICE—

THAT DOES IT!

THE JAP CAMP GUARD AWOKE.

FIRE!

FIRE IN THE HOLE!

JUNGLI'S RAIDERS PULLED OUT — JUST IN TIME.

NOW WE LAY A FEW BOOBY-TRAPS FOR ANY NIPS THAT COME SNIFFING AFTER US.

DAYBREAK—

NO MORE JAPONI. TAKE US STRAIGHT TO KOHIMA ON BIG ROAD — YOU MALUM?

KOHIMA! MALUM.

TWO HOURS LATER —

THEY SEEM FRIENDLY. WE'RE GETTING A NOISY WELCOME.

MY BOOBY-TRAPS! TIME WE GOT MOVING.

FOR THREE DAYS AND TWO NIGHTS THE PARTY MOVED THROUGH THE NAGA HILLS, ON THE THIRD EVENING —

ALBERT, I KEEP TELLING YOU IT'S AGAINST KING'S REGULATIONS TO KEEP A DIARY IN ACTION.

THIS AIN'T A DIARY, JUNGLI — JUST A BIT OF SCRIBBLE TO AMUSE MYSELF.

JAPONI COME!

PACK UP, BLOKES! WE'RE AWAY!

THE NAGAS LED THE WAY THROUGH THE ENCLOSING RICE TERRACES . . .

FIRING! THE NIPS ARE IN THE VILLAGE ALREADY.

JAPONI!

THEY'RE ALL AROUND US.

THE GROUP WENT TO GROUND . . .

BUT BEFORE THEY MOVED ON . . .

SOMEBODY'S MISSING.

BABU NOT HERE. HE IS GOING FOR TRADING CURRY IN VILLAGE.

THEN CAME THE RATTLE OF MACHINE-GUN FIRE FROM THE VILLAGE.

THAT'S A PUNISHMENT FOR HELPING US! AND I SEE HOW THE NIPS KNOW THOSE PEOPLE HELPED US . . .

THEY'VE GOT BABU!

JUNGLI'S PARTY WATCHED FOR AN HOUR AS JAP SQUADS LEFT THE VILLAGE.

MORE OF THEM MOVING OUT. CAN'T BE MORE THAN A HEADQUARTERS STAFF LEFT IN THE VILLAGE.

TIME WE MOVED TOO. PACK UP.

JUNGLI, ME AND THESE BLOKES WANT A SHOT AT HELPING BABU.

AND RISK THE WHOLE PARTY FOR ONE MAN? THAT IS JUST WHAT I AIN'T DOING.

POST MY LITTLE BOOK TO MY MA IN CASE I DON'T GET BACK.

HUH?

WONDER WHAT THAT FOUR-EYED TWIT'S BEEN SCRIBBLING ABOUT!

"IT'S A COMFORT BEING AROUND A REAL SOLDIER LIKE MY MATE JUNGLI, SO COOL AND STEADY, NEVER FLAPPING" — IS THAT HOW THE LITTLE TWIRP SEES ME?

FIVE MINUTES LATER —

HEY — WAIT FOR ME! YOU DON'T THINK I'D LET YOU LOT GO OFF ALONE, DO YER?

JUNGLI'S RAIDERS CLOSED IN ON THE VILLAGE —

WE GOT A CHANCE IF I CAN GET ME HANDS ON THEIR WOODPECKER MACHINE-GUN, BUT FIRST WE HAVE A JOB FOR THE NAGAS . . .

THE JOB FOR THE NAGAS.

THAT'S RIGHT! LOOK THIS WAY, JAPONI!

JUNGLI OPENED UP WITH THE WOODPECKER.

ALBERT, GO GET BABU WHILE I COVER YOU.

WITH THE JAPS PROWLER GUARD TAKEN CARE OF, THE RAIDERS CHARGED.

121

ALL RIGHT, BABU?

LIKE THEY ARE SAYING IN MOVING PICTURE — IT IS ONLY HURTING WHEN I LAUGH.

GUN'S JAMMED — A SPLIT CASE. JAP RUBBISH!

BETTER CLEAR IT QUICK, MATE. LOOK WHAT'S COMING.

BANZAIIIII!

BUT THEN THE NAGA WARRIORS JOINED THE FIGHT.

JAM CLEARED, BUT LOOKS LIKE WE AIN'T GOING TO NEED THE OLD WOODPECKER AGAIN.

JUNGLI — LOOK OUT!

KILL MY MATE, WOULD YER?

REALISING JUNGLI COULD NOT MOVE OUT OF THE WAY IN TIME, ALBERT THREW HIMSELF FORWARD.

ARGH!

ALBERT! OH NO — NO!

122

123